Coincraft's Coi[illegible]

1816 to Date

Richard Lobel
Allan Hailstone
Eleni Calligas

London 1998

Published by Standard Catalogue Publishers Ltd for Coincraft

Database typeset by BPC Whitefriars Ltd;
printed and bound by BPC Wheatons Ltd.
Both members of the British Printing Company Ltd.

ISBN 0 9526228 31

Contents

Hello and Welcome!

Welcome to *Coincraft's Coin Checklist*, covering all the British coins and sets issued from 1816 to date. The reason for picking 1816 for a starting date was the Currency Reform Act of 1816, which set the rules governing all the coins that were issued from that date on — the size, the weight and even the fineness.

The last check listing of British coins was issued about 1971 and it literally just covered the change in your pocket. We have covered the entire series including a lot of coins which neither you nor I can afford. Well, perhaps one day we will win the lottery...!

This is a handy sized book which you can carry with you and it will actually let you know what you own and what you need. There are descriptions of all the coins, plus spaces for the condition of the coins you have, the prices you paid, who you bought them from and what those coins are worth today. It also includes of course the Standard Catalogue numbers as well, so you can tick the exact coins that you have in your collection. It is much easier than carrying a big book along with you.

If you need extra copies they are available from either your local dealer or from Coincraft; the price is £6.95 including postage.

Enjoy this book and use it to keep track of your coin collection; it is a nice handy size so you can carry it to coin fairs and auctions.

Stay well, be happy and keep on collecting.

Richard Lobel

P.S. By using this checklist, you might just find that your collection is worth more than you thought!

Five Pounds

George IV 1820 – 1830

✓	No.	Date	Features	*Grade*	*Purchased From*	*Date*	*Price Paid*	*Value Now*
	G45P-005	1826	PROOF					
	G45P-010	1826	PROOF; edge plain					
	G45P-015	1826	PROOF on thick flan; edge plain					
	G45P-020	1829	PROOF or pattern; edge plain					

Victoria 1837 – 1901

Young Head

✓	No.	Date	Features	*Grade*	*Purchased From*	*Date*	*Price Paid*	*Value Now*
	VY5P-005	1839	rev. DIRIGE; edge lettered					
	VY5P-010	1839	rev. DIRIGE; edge plain					
	VY5P-015	1839	rev. DIRIGIT; edge lettered					
	VY5P-020	1839	rev. DIRIGIT; edge plain					

Jubilee Head

✓	No.	Date	Features	*Grade*	*Purchased From*	*Date*	*Price Paid*	*Value Now*
	VJ5P-025	1887						
	VJ5P-030	1887	PROOF					
	VJ5P-035	1887	PROOF; no B.P. in exergue					

Old Head

✓	No.	Date	Features	*Grade*	*Purchased From*	*Date*	*Price Paid*	*Value Now*
	VO5P-040	1893						
	VO5P-045	1893	PROOF					

Edward VII 1901 – 1910

✓	No.	Date	Features	*Grade*	*Purchased From*	*Date*	*Price Paid*	*Value Now*
	E75P-005	1902						
	E75P-010	1902	matt PROOF					

George V 1910 – 1936

✓	No.	Date	Features	*Grade*	*Purchased From*	*Date*	*Price Paid*	*Value Now*
	G55P-005	1911	PROOF					

Edward VIII 1936

✓	No.	Date	Features	*Grade*	*Purchased From*	*Date*	*Price Paid*	*Value Now*
	E85P-005	1937						

George VI 1937 – 1952

✓	No.	Date	Features	*Grade*	*Purchased From*	*Date*	*Price Paid*	*Value Now*
	G65P-005	1937	PROOF					

Elizabeth II 1952 –

✓	No.	Date	Features	*Grade*	*Purchased From*	*Date*	*Price Paid*	*Value Now*
	EL25P-005	1953	PROOF or pattern					
	EL25P-010	1957	PROOF					
	EL25P-015	1980	PROOF					
	EL25P-020	1981	PROOF					
	EL25P-025	1982	PROOF					
	EL25P-030	1984						
	EL25P-035	1984	PROOF					
	EL25P-040	1985						
	EL25P-045	1985	PROOF					
	EL25P-050	1986						
	EL25P-055	1987						
	EL25P-060	1988						
	EL25P-065	1989						
	EL25P-070	1989	PROOF					
	EL25P-075	1990						
	EL25P-080	1990	PROOF					
	EL25P-085	1991						
	EL25P-090	1991	PROOF					
	EL25P-095	1992						
	EL25P-100	1992	PROOF					
	EL25P-105	1993						
	EL25P-110	1993	PROOF					
	EL25P-115	1994						
	EL25P-120	1994	PROOF					
	EL25P-125	1995						
	EL25P-130	1995	PROOF					
	EL25P-135	1996						
	EL25P-140	1996	PROOF					
	EL25P-145	1997						
	EL25P-150	1997	PROOF					

Two Pounds

George IV 1820 – 1830

✓	No.	Date	Features	*Grade*	*Purchased From*	*Date*	*Price Paid*	*Value Now*
	G42P-005	1823						
	G42P-010	1823	PROOF					
	G42P-015	1825	PROOF or pattern; edge plain					
	G42P-020	1826	PROOF					
	G42P-025	1826	PROOF on thick flan; edge plain					

William IV 1830 – 1837

✓	No.	Date	Features	*Grade*	*Purchased From*	*Date*	*Price Paid*	*Value Now*
	W42P-005	1831	PROOF					

Victoria 1837 – 1901

Jubilee Head

✓	No.	Date	Features	*Grade*	*Purchased From*	*Date*	*Price Paid*	*Value Now*
	VJ2P-005	1887						
	VJ2P-010	1887	PROOF					
	VJ2P-015	1887	PROOF; no B.P. in exergue					

Old Head

✓	No.	Date	Features	*Grade*	*Purchased From*	*Date*	*Price Paid*	*Value Now*
	VO2P-020	1893						
	VO2P-025	1893	PROOF					

Edward VII 1901 – 1910

✓	No.	Date	Features	*Grade*	*Purchased From*	*Date*	*Price Paid*	*Value Now*
	E72P-005	1902						
	E72P-010	1902	matt PROOF					

George V 1910 – 1936

✓	No.	Date	Features	*Grade*	*Purchased From*	*Date*	*Price Paid*	*Value Now*
	G52P-005	1911	PROOF					

Edward VIII 1936

✓	No.	Date	Features	*Grade*	*Purchased From*	*Date*	*Price Paid*	*Value Now*
	E82P-005	1937						

George VI 1937 – 1952

✓	No.	Date	Features	*Grade*	*Purchased From*	*Date*	*Price Paid*	*Value Now*
	G62P-005	1937	PROOF					

Elizabeth II 1952 –

✓	No.	Date	Features	*Grade*	*Purchased From*	*Date*	*Price Paid*	*Value Now*
	EL22P-005	1953	PROOF or pattern					
	EL22P-010	1980	PROOF					
	EL22P-015	1982	PROOF					
	EL22P-020	1983	PROOF					
	EL22P-025	1985	PROOF					
	EL22P-030	1986	PROOF					
	EL22P-035	1987	PROOF					
	EL22P-040	1988	PROOF					
	EL22P-045	1989	PROOF					
	EL22P-050	1990	PROOF					
	EL22P-055	1991	PROOF					
	EL22P-060	1992	PROOF					
	EL22P-065	1993	PROOF					
	EL22P-070	1994	PROOF					
	EL22P-075	1994	PROOF					
	EL22P-080	1995	PROOF					
	EL22P-085	1995	PROOF					
	EL22P-090	1996	PROOF					
	EL22P-095	1997	PROOF					

Sovereign

George III 1760 – 1820

✓	No.	Date	Features	*Grade*	*Purchased From*	*Date*	*Price Paid*	*Value Now*
	G3SV-005	1817						
	G3SV-010	1817	PROOF					
	G3SV-015	1818						
	G3SV-020	1818	PROOF					
	G3SV-025	1819						
	G3SV-030	1820						

George IV 1820 – 1830

✓	No.	Date	Features	*Grade*	*Purchased From*	*Date*	*Price Paid*	*Value Now*
	G4SV-005	1821						
	G4SV-010	1821	PROOF					
	G4SV-015	1822						
	G4SV-020	1823						
	G4SV-025	1824						
	G4SV-030	1825	obv. 1, rev. 1					
	G4SV-035	1825	obv. 2, rev. 2					
	G4SV-040	1825	PROOF; edge plain					
	G4SV-045	1826						
	G4SV-050	1826	PROOF					
	G4SV-055	1827						
	G4SV-060	1828						
	G4SV-065	1829						
	G4SV-070	1830						

William IV 1830 – 1837

✓	No.	Date	Features	*Grade*	*Purchased From*	*Date*	*Price Paid*	*Value Now*
	W4SV-005	1831						
	W4SV-010	1831	PROOF; edge plain					
	W4SV-015	1831	WW without stops (obv.)					
	W4SV-020	1832						
	W4SV-025	1832	PROOF					
	W4SV-030	1832	WW without stops (obv.)					
	W4SV-035	1833						
	W4SV-040	1835						
	W4SV-045	1836						
	W4SV-048	1836	raised 'N' on shield above ANNO (rev.)					
	W4SV-050	1837						

Victoria 1837 – 1901

Young Head

Rev. 1, 2, 3 = Shield
Rev. 4 = St George

✓	No.	Date	Features	*Grade*	*Purchased From*	*Date*	*Price Paid*	*Value Now*
	VYSV-005	1838						
	VYSV-010	1838	PROOF; edge plain					
	VYSV-015	1838	PROOF; edge plain; rev. ↓					
	VYSV-020	1839						
	VYSV-025	1839	PROOF; rev.1					
	VYSV-030	1839	PROOF; edge plain					
	VYSV-035	1839	PROOF; edge plain; rev. ↓					
	VYSV-040	1839	PROOF; rev. 3					
	VYSV-045	1841						
	VYSV-050	1842						
	VYSV-055	1843	rev. 1					
	VYSV-060	1843	3 over 2					
	VYSV-065	1843	rev. 2					
	VYSV-070	1844						
	VYSV-075	1844	first 4 over inverted 4					
	VYSV-080	1845						
	VYSV-085	1846						
	VYSV-090	1847						
	VYSV-095	1848	obv. 1, rev. 1					
	VYSV-100	1848	obv. 2, rev. 3					
	VYSV-105	1849						
	VYSV-110	1850						
	VYSV-115	1851						
	VYSV-120	1852						
	VYSV-125	1853	obv. 2					
	VYSV-130	1853	obv. 3					
	VYSV-135	1853	PROOF					
	VYSV-140	1853	PROOF; rev. ↓					
	VYSV-145	1854	obv. 2					
	VYSV-150	1854	obv. 3					
	VYSV-155	1855	obv. 2					
	VYSV-160	1855	obv. 3					
	VYSV-165	1856						
	VYSV-170	1857						
	VYSV-175	1858						
	VYSV-180	1859						
	VYSV-185	1859	'Ansell' type					
	VYSV-190	1860						
	VYSV-195	1861						
	VYSV-200	1862						
	VYSV-205	1863	no die number					
	VYSV-210	1863	no die number '827' in raised numerals on truncation instead of 'WW' (obv.)					
	VYSV-215	1863	die number					

Cont.

✓	No.	Date	Features	Grade	Purchased From	Date	Price Paid	Value Now
	VYSV-220	1863	die number 22, '827' on truncation instead of 'WW' (obv.)					
	VYSV-225	1864	die number					
	VYSV-230	1864	PROOF raised 'I' to left of incuse 'WW' (obv.)					
	VYSV-235	1865	die number					
	VYSV-240	1866	die number					
	VYSV-245	1868	die number					
	VYSV-250	1869	die number					
	VYSV-255	1870	die number; obv. 3					
	VYSV-260	1870	die number; obv. 5					
	VYSV-265	1871	die number; obv. 5, rev. 3					
	VYSV-270	1871	obv. 6, rev. 4					
	VYSV-275	1871	PROOF					
	VYSV-280	1871	PROOF; rev. ↓					
	VYSV-285	1871	PROOF; edge plain; rev. ↓					
	VYSV-290	1872	no die number, rev. 3					
	VYSV-295	1872	die number, rev. 3					
	VYSV-300	1872	rev. 4					
	VYSV-305	1873	die number; rev. 3					
	VYSV-310	1873	rev. 4					
	VYSV-315	1874	die number; rev. 3					
	VYSV-320	1874	rev. 4					
	VYSV-325	1876						
	VYSV-330	1878						
	VYSV-335	1879						
	VYSV-338	1879	PROOF					
	VYSV-340	1880	PROOF; edge plain; rev. 3					
	VYSV-345	1880	with B.P.					
	VYSV-350	1880	no B.P.					
	VYSV-355	1880	PROOF					
	VYSV-360	1884	obv. 6					
	VYSV-365	1884	obv. 7					
	VYSV-370	1885	obv. 6					
	VYSV-375	1885	obv. 7					
	VYSV-380	1887	PROOF					
	VYSV-385	1887	PROOF; edge plain					

Jubilee Head

✓	No.	Date	Features	Grade	Purchased From	Date	Price Paid	Value Now
	VJSV-390	1887						
	VJSV-395	1887	PROOF					
	VJSV-400	1888						
	VJSV-405	1889						
	VJSV-410	1890						
	VJSV-415	1891						
	VJSV-420	1891	PROOF in lead					
	VJSV-425	1892						

Old Head

✓	No.	Date	Features	Grade	Purchased From	Date	Price Paid	Value Now
	VOSV-430	1893						
	VOSV-435	1893	PROOF					
	VOSV-440	1894						
	VOSV-445	1895						
	VOSV-450	1896						
	VOSV-455	1898						
	VOSV-460	1899						
	VOSV-465	1900						
	VOSV-470	1901						

Edward VII 1901 – 1910

✓	No.	Date	Features	Grade	Purchased From	Date	Price Paid	Value Now
	E7SV-005	1902						
	E7SV-010	1902	matt PROOF					
	E7SV-015	1903						
	E7SV-020	1904						
	E7SV-025	1905						
	E7SV-030	1906						
	E7SV-035	1906	matt PROOF					
	E7SV-040	1907						
	E7SV-045	1908						
	E7SV-050	1909						
	E7SV-055	1910						

George V 1910 – 1936

✓	No.	Date	Features	Grade	Purchased From	Date	Price Paid	Value Now
	G5SV-005	1911						
	G5SV-010	1911	PROOF					
	G5SV-015	1912						
	G5SV-020	1913						
	G5SV-025	1914						
	G5SV-030	1915						
	G5SV-035	1916						
	G5SV-040	1917						
	G5SV-045	1925						

Edward VIII 1936

✓	No.	Date	Features	Grade	Purchased From	Date	Price Paid	Value Now
	E8SV-005	1937						

George VI 1937 – 1952

✓	No.	Date	Features	Grade	Purchased From	Date	Price Paid	Value Now
	G6SV-005	1937	PROOF					

Elizabeth II 1952 –

✓	No.	Date	Features	Grade	Purchased From	Date	Price Paid	Value Now
	EL2SV-005	1953	PROOF or pattern					
	EL2SV-010	1957						
	EL2SV-015	1957	PROOF					
	EL2SV-020	1958						
	EL2SV-025	1958	PROOF					
	EL2SV-030	1959						
	EL2SV-035	1962						
	EL2SV-040	1963						
	EL2SV-045	1964						
	EL2SV-050	1965						
	EL2SV-055	1966						
	EL2SV-060	1967						
	EL2SV-065	1968						
	EL2SV-070	1974						
	EL2SV-075	1976						
	EL2SV-080	1978						
	EL2SV-085	1979						
	EL2SV-090	1979	PROOF					
	EL2SV-095	1980						
	EL2SV-100	1980	PROOF					
	EL2SV-105	1981						
	EL2SV-110	1981	PROOF					
	EL2SV-115	1982						
	EL2SV-120	1982	PROOF					
	EL2SV-125	1983	PROOF					
	EL2SV-130	1984	PROOF					
	EL2SV-135	1985	PROOF					
	EL2SV-140	1986	PROOF					
	EL2SV-145	1987	PROOF					
	EL2SV-150	1988	PROOF					
	EL2SV-155	1989	PROOF					
	EL2SV-160	1990	PROOF					
	EL2SV-165	1991	PROOF					
	EL2SV-170	1992	PROOF					
	EL2SV-175	1993	PROOF					
	EL2SV-180	1994	PROOF					
	EL2SV-185	1995	PROOF					
	EL2SV-190	1996	PROOF					
	EL2SV-195	1997	PROOF					

Half Sovereign

George III 1760 – 1820

✓	No.	Date	Features	*Grade*	*Purchased From*	*Date*	*Price Paid*	*Value Now*
	G3HS-005	1817						
	G3HS-010	1817	PROOF					
	G3HS-015	1818						
	G3HS-020	1818	latter 8 over 7					
	G3HS-025	1818	PROOF					
	G3HS-030	1820						

George IV 1820 – 1830

✓	No.	Date	Features	*Grade*	*Purchased From*	*Date*	*Price Paid*	*Value Now*
	G4HS-005	1821						
	G4HS-010	1821	PROOF					
	G4HS-015	1823						
	G4HS-020	1823	PROOF					
	G4HS-025	1824						
	G4HS-030	1825						
	G4HS-035	1825	PROOF					
	G4HS-040	1825	PROOF; edge plain					
	G4HS-045	1826						
	G4HS-050	1826	PROOF					
	G4HS-055	1827						
	G4HS-060	1828						

William IV 1830 – 1837

✓	No.	Date	Features	*Grade*	*Purchased From*	*Date*	*Price Paid*	*Value Now*
	W4HS-005	1831	PROOF edge plain					
	W4HS-010	1834						
	W4HS-015	1835						
	W4HS-020	1836	obv. 2					
	W4HS-025	1836	obv. 3					
	W4HS-030	1837	obv. 2					
	W4HS-035	1837	obv. 3					

Victoria 1837 – 1901

Young Head

✓	No.	Date	Features	*Grade*	*Purchased From*	*Date*	*Price Paid*	*Value Now*
	VYHS-005	1838						
	VYHS-010	1839	PROOF; edge plain					
	VYHS-015	1839	PROOF; edge plain; rev.↓					
	VYHS-020	1839	PROOF in silver; edge plain					

✓	No.	Date	Features	*Grade*	*Purchased From*	*Date*	*Price Paid*	*Value Now*
	VYHS-025	1841						
	VYHS-030	1842						
	VYHS-035	1843						
	VYHS-040	1844						
	VYHS-045	1845						
	VYHS-050	1846						
	VYHS-055	1847						
	VYHS-060	1848						
	VYHS-065	1848	latter 8 over 7					
	VYHS-070	1849						
	VYHS-075	1850						
	VYHS-080	1851						
	VYHS-085	1852						
	VYHS-090	1853						
	VYHS-095	1853	PROOF					
	VYHS-100	1854						
	VYHS-105	1855						
	VYHS-110	1856						
	VYHS-115	1857						
	VYHS-120	1858						
	VYHS-125	1859						
	VYHS-130	1860						
	VYHS-135	1861						
	VYHS-140	1862						
	VYHS-145	1863	no die number					
	VYHS-150	1863	die number					
	VYHS-155	1864	die number					
	VYHS-160	1865	die number					
	VYHS-165	1866	die number					
	VYHS-170	1867	die number					
	VYHS-175	1869	die number					
	VYHS-180	1870	die number					
	VYHS-185	1871	die number					
	VYHS-190	1871	PROOF; die number					
	VYHS-195	1871	PROOF; edge plain; die number					
	VYHS-200	1872	die number					
	VYHS-205	1873	die number					
	VYHS-210	1874	die number					
	VYHS-215	1875	die number					
	VYHS-220	1876	die number					
	VYHS-225	1876	die number					
	VYHS-230	1877	die number; obv. 1					
	VYHS-232	1877	PROOF; die number					
	VYHS-235	1877	die number; obv. 2					
	VYHS-240	1878	die number					
	VYHS-245	1878	PROOF; die number					
	VYHS-250	1879	die number					
	VYHS-255	1880	die number; obv. 2					
	VYHS-260	1880	die number; obv. 3					
	VYHS-265	1880	no die number					
	VYHS-270	1880	PROOF; no die number					

Cont.

✓	No.	Date	Features	Grade	Purchased From	Date	Price Paid	Value Now
	VYHS-275	1883						
	VYHS-280	1884						
	VYHS-285	1885						
	VYHS-290	1886	PROOF					
	VYHS-292	1887	PROOF					

Jubilee Head

✓	No.	Date	Features	Grade	Purchased From	Date	Price Paid	Value Now
	VJHS-295	1887	obv. 4					
	VJHS-300	1887	PROOF					
	VJHS-305	1887	obv. 5					
	VJHS-310	1888						
	VJHS-315	1890						
	VJHS-320	1890						
	VJHS-325	1891						
	VJHS-330	1892						
	VJHS-335	1893						

Old Head

✓	No.	Date	Features	Grade	Purchased From	Date	Price Paid	Value Now
	VOHS-345	1893	PROOF					
	VOHS-350	1894						
	VOHS-355	1895						
	VOHS-360	1896						
	VOHS-365	1897						
	VOHS-370	1898						
	VOHS-375	1899						
	VOHS-380	1900						
	VOHS-385	1901						

Edward VII 1901 – 1910

✓	No.	Date	Features	Grade	Purchased From	Date	Price Paid	Value Now
	E7HS-005	1902						
	E7HS-010	1902	matt PROOF					
	E7HS-015	1903						
	E7HS-020	1904	rev. 1					
	E7HS-025	1904	rev. 2					
	E7HS-030	1905						
	E7HS-035	1906						
	E7HS-040	1906	matt PROOF					
	E7HS-045	1907						
	E7HS-050	1908						
	E7HS-055	1909						
	E7HS-060	1910						

George V 1910 – 1936

✓	No.	Date	Features	*Grade*	*Purchased From*	*Date*	*Price Paid*	*Value Now*
	G5HS-005	1911						
	G5HS-010	1911	PROOF					
	G5HS-015	1912						
	G5HS-020	1913						
	G5HS-025	1914						
	G5HS-030	1915						

George VI 1937 – 1952

✓	No.	Date	Features	*Grade*	*Purchased From*	*Date*	*Price Paid*	*Value Now*
	G6HS-005	1937	PROOF					

Elizabeth II 1952 –

✓	No.	Date	Features	*Grade*	*Purchased From*	*Date*	*Price Paid*	*Value Now*
	EL2HS-005	1953	PROOF or pattern					
	EL2HS-010	1980	PROOF					
	EL2HS-015	1982						
	EL2HS-020	1982	PROOF					
	EL2HS-025	1983	PROOF					
	EL2HS-030	1984	PROOF					
	EL2HS-035	1985	PROOF					
	EL2HS-040	1986	PROOF					
	EL2HS-045	1987	PROOF					
	EL2HS-050	1988	PROOF					
	EL2HS-055	1989	PROOF					
	EL2HS-060	1990	PROOF					
	EL2HS-065	1991	PROOF					
	EL2HS-070	1992	PROOF					
	EL2HS-075	1993	PROOF					
	EL2HS-080	1994	PROOF					
	EL2HS-085	1995	PROOF					
	EL2HS-090	1996	PROOF					
	EL2HS-095	1997	PROOF					

Crown

George III 1760 – 1820

✓	No.	Date	Features	*Grade*	*Purchased From*	*Date*	*Price Paid*	*Value Now*
	G3CR-200	1818	edge LVIII					
	G3CR-205	1818	PROOF; edge LVIII					
	G3CR-210	1818	edge DECVS ANNO REGNI ET TVTAMEN; edge LVIII					
	G3CR-215	1818	edge LIX					
	G3CR-220	1819	edge LIX					
	G3CR-225	1819	9 over 8; edge LIX					
	G3CR-230	1819	no edge stops; edge LIX					
	G3CR-235	1819	edge LX					
	G3CR-240	1819	PROOF; edge LX					
	G3CR-245	1819	PROOF; edge plain					
	G3CR-250	1820						
	G3CR-255	1820	20 over 19					
	G3CR-260	1820	S of SOIT over T (rev.)					
	G3CR-265	1820	PROOF					

George IV 1820 – 1830

✓	No.	Date	Features	*Grade*	*Purchased From*	*Date*	*Price Paid*	*Value Now*
	G4CR-005	1821	edge SECUNDO					
	G4CR-010	1821	WWP initials inverted (rev.); edge SECUNDO					
	G4CR-015	1821	PROOF; edge SECUNDO					
	G4CR-020	1821	PROOF in copper; edge SECUNDO					
	G4CR-025	1821	PROOF in copper; edge plain					
	G4CR-030	1821	PROOF; edge TERTIO					
	G4CR-035	1822	edge SECUNDO					
	G4CR-040	1822	PROOF; edge SECUNDO					
	G4CR-045	1822	edge TERTIO					
	G4CR-050	1822	PROOF; edge TERTIO					
	G4CR-055	1823	PROOF; edge plain					
	G4CR-060	1823	PROOF in white metal; edge plain					
	G4CR-065	1825	PROOF or pattern; edge plain					
	G4CR-070	1825	PROOF or pattern in Barton's metal; edge plain					
	G4CR-075	1826	PROOF; edge SEPTIMO					
	G4CR-080	1826	PROOF; edge plain					
	G4CR-085	1826	PROOF (?); edge LVIII					

William IV 1830 – 1837

✓	No.	Date	Features	*Grade*	*Purchased From*	*Date*	*Price Paid*	*Value Now*
	W4CR-005	1831	PROOF; obv. 1; edge plain					
	W4CR-010	1831	PROOF in gold; edge plain					
	W4CR-015	1831	PROOF; obv. 2; edge plain					

✓	No.	Date	Features	*Grade*	*Purchased From*	*Date*	*Price Paid*	*Value Now*
	W4CR-020	1831	PROOF; obv. 2; edge plain; rev. ↓					
	W4CR-025	1832	PROOF in lead					
	W4CR-030	1834	PROOF; edge plain					

Victoria 1837 – 1901

Young Head

✓	No.	Date	Features	*Grade*	*Purchased From*	*Date*	*Price Paid*	*Value Now*
	VYCR-005	1839	PROOF; edge plain					
	VYCR-010	1844						
	VYCR-015	1844	edge inscription struck twice in different positions					
	VYCR-020	1844	PROOF					
	VYCR-025	1845						
	VYCR-028	1845	4 in date has large upper serif					
	VYCR-030	1845	AANNO instead of ANNO (edge)					
	VYCR-035	1845	PROOF					
	VYCR-040	1845	PROOF; edge plain					
	VYCR-045	1845	PROOF; edge plain; rev. ↓					
	VYCR-050	1847						
	VYCR-055	1847	edge milled					

'Gothic' issue

✓	No.	Date	Features	*Grade*	*Purchased From*	*Date*	*Price Paid*	*Value Now*
	VGCR-060	1847	PROOF; edge UNDECIMO					
	VGCR-065	1847	PROOF in fine silver; heavily frosted; rev. ↓; edge UNDECIMO					
	VGCR-070	1847	PROOF; edge plain; rev. ↓					
	VGCR-075	1847	PROOF, frosted; edge UNDECIMO					
	VGCR-080	1847	PROOF; edges chamfered; lettering weak; rev. ↓; edge UNDECIMO					
	VGCR-085	1847	PROOF in gold; edge plain					
	VGCR-090	1847	PROOF in white metal; edge plain					
	VGCR-095	1847	PROOF; rev. ↓; edge DECIMO SEPTIMO					
	VGCR-100	1853	PROOF					
	VGCR-105	1853	PROOF; edge plain					

Young Head

✓	No.	Date	Features	*Grade*	*Purchased From*	*Date*	*Price Paid*	*Value Now*
	VYCR-110	1879	PROOF; edge plain					

Jubilee Head

✓	No.	Date	Features	*Grade*	*Purchased From*	*Date*	*Price Paid*	*Value Now*
	VJCR-115	1887						
	VJCR-120	1887	PROOF					
	VJCR-125	1888						
	VJCR-130	1888	narrow date					

Cont.

✓	No.	Date	Features	Grade	Purchased From	Date	Price Paid	Value Now
	VJCR-135	1889						
	VJCR-140	1890						
	VJCR-145	1891						
	VJCR-150	1892						

Old Head

✓	No.	Date	Features	Grade	Purchased From	Date	Price Paid	Value Now
	VOCR-155	1893	edge LVI					
	VOCR-160	1893	PROOF; edge LVI					
	VOCR-165	1893	edge LVII					
	VOCR-170	1894	edge LVII					
	VOCR-175	1894	edge LVIII					
	VOCR-180	1895	edge LVIII					
	VOCR-185	1895	edge LIX					
	VOCR-190	1896	edge LIX					
	VOCR-195	1896	edge LX					
	VOCR-200	1897	edge LX					
	VOCR-205	1897	edge LXI					
	VOCR-210	1898	edge LXI					
	VOCR-215	1898	edge LXII					
	VOCR-220	1899	edge LXII					
	VOCR-225	1899	edge LXIII					
	VOCR-230	1900	edge LXIII					
	VOCR-235	1900	edge LXIV					

Edward VII 1901 – 1910

✓	No.	Date	Features	Grade	Purchased From	Date	Price Paid	Value Now
	E7CR-005	1902						
	E7CR-010	1902	matt PROOF					

George V 1910 – 1936

'Wreath' Issue

✓	No.	Date	Features	Grade	Purchased From	Date	Price Paid	Value Now
	G5CR-005	1927	PROOF					
	G5CR-010	1927	PROOF from sandblasted dies					
	G5CR-015	1928						
	G5CR-020	1928	PROOF					
	G5CR-025	1929						
	G5CR-030	1929	PROOF					
	G5CR-035	1930						
	G5CR-040	1930	PROOF					
	G5CR-045	1931						
	G5CR-050	1931	PROOF					
	G5CR-055	1932						
	G5CR-060	1932	PROOF					
	G5CR-065	1933						

Cont.

✓	No.	Date	Features	*Grade*	*Purchased From*	*Date*	*Price Paid*	*Value Now*
	G5CR-070	1933	PROOF					
	G5CR-075	1934						
	G5CR-080	1934	PROOF					

Jubilee Issue

✓	No.	Date	Features	*Grade*	*Purchased From*	*Date*	*Price Paid*	*Value Now*
	G5CR-085	1935						
	G5CR-090	1935	edge error					
	G5CR-095	1935	SPECIMEN					
	G5CR-100	1935	PROOF in sterling silver					
	G5CR-105	1935	PROOF; raised edge lettering					
	G5CR-110	1935	PROOF; raised error edge lettering reads DECUS ANNO REGNI ET TVTAMEN. XXV					
	G5CR-115	1935	PROOF or pattern with edge inscription in finer lettering					
	G5CR-120	1935	PROOF in gold; raised edge lettering					

'Wreath' Issue

✓	No.	Date	Features	*Grade*	*Purchased From*	*Date*	*Price Paid*	*Value Now*
	G5CR-125	1936						
	G5CR-130	1936	PROOF					

Edward VIII 1936

✓	No.	Date	Features	*Grade*	*Purchased From*	*Date*	*Price Paid*	*Value Now*
	E8CR-005	1937						

George VI 1937 – 1952

✓	No.	Date	Features	*Grade*	*Purchased From*	*Date*	*Price Paid*	*Value Now*
	G6CR-005	1937						
	G6CR-010	1937	PROOF					
	G6CR-015	1937	PROOF heavily frosted					
	G6CR-020	1937	PROOF from sandblasted dies					
	G6CR-025	1951	PROOF					
	G6CR-028	1951	PROOF; edge lettering blundered					
	G6CR-030	1951	PROOF, heavily frosted with brilliant field					
	G6CR-035	1951	PROOF from sandblasted dies					
	G6CR-040	1951	PROOF; edge plain					

Elizabeth II 1952 –

✓	No.	Date	Features	*Grade*	*Purchased From*	*Date*	*Price Paid*	*Value Now*
	EL2CR-005	1953						
	EL2CR-010	1953	YO instead of YOU (edge)					
	EL2CR-015	1953	PROOF					

Cont.

✓	No.	Date	Features	*Grade*	*Purchased From*	*Date*	*Price Paid*	*Value Now*
	EL2CR-020	1953	PROOF from sandblasted dies					
	EL2CR-025	1960						
	EL2CR-030	1960	polished die specimen					
	EL2CR-035	1960	PROOF frosted bust					
	EL2CR-040	1965						
	EL2CR-045	1965	satin finish					

Double Florin

Victoria 1837 – 1901

✓	No.	Date	Features	*Grade*	*Purchased From*	*Date*	*Price Paid*	*Value Now*
	VJDFL-005	1887	Roman I in date; obv. 1					
	VJDFL-010	1887	PROOF Roman I in date; obv. 1					
	VJDFL-015	1887	Arabic 1 in date; obv. 1					
	VJDFL-020	1887	Arabic 1 in date; obv. 2					
	VJDFL-025	1887	PROOF Arabic 1 in date; obv. 2					
	VJDFL-030	1888						
	VJDFL-035	1888	second I in VICTORIA is inverted '1'					
	VJDFL-040	1889						
	VJDFL-045	1889	second I in VICTORIA is inverted '1'					
	VJDFL-050	1890						

Three Shillings

George III 1760 – 1820

✓	No.	Date	Features	*Grade*	*Purchased From*	*Date*	*Price Paid*	*Value Now*
	G33S-005	1811						
	G33S-010	1811	PROOF					
	G33S-015	1812	obv. 1, rev. 1					
	G33S-020	1812	obv. 2, rev. 2					
	G33S-025	1812	PROOF					
	G33S-030	1812	PROOF in gold					
	G33S-035	1812	PROOF in platinum					
	G33S-040	1813						
	G33S-045	1814						
	G33S-050	1815						
	G33S-055	1816						

Halfcrown

George III 1760 – 1820

✓	No.	Date	Features	*Grade*	*Purchased From*	*Date*	*Price Paid*	*Value Now*
	G3HC-035	1816						
	G3HC-040	1816	PROOF					
	G3HC-045	1816	PROOF; edge plain					
	G3HC-050	1817	obv. 1, rev. 1					
	G3HC-055	1817	D of DEI over T (obv.); obv. 1, rev. 1					
	G3HC-058	1817	S of PENSE over I (rev.)					
	G3HC-060	1817	PROOF; obv. 1, rev. 1					
	G3HC-065	1817	PROOF; edge plain; obv. 1, rev. 1					
	G3HC-070	1817	PROOF in copper; obv. 1, rev. 1					
	G3HC-075	1817	obv. 2, rev. 2					
	G3HC-080	1817	each 'S' in Garter motto reversed (rev.); obv. 2, rev. 2					
	G3HC-085	1817	PROOF; obv. 2, rev. 2					
	G3HC-090	1817	PROOF; edge plain; obv. 2, rev. 2					
	G3HC-095	1818						
	G3HC-098	1818	'S' in garter motto reversed (rev.)					
	G3HC-100	1818	PROOF					
	G3HC-105	1819						
	G3HC-110	1819	9 over 8					
	G3HC-115	1819	PROOF					
	G3HC-120	1820						
	G3HC-125	1820	PROOF					
	G3HC-130	1820	PROOF; edge plain					

George IV 1820 – 1830

✓	No.	Date	Features	*Grade*	*Purchased From*	*Date*	*Price Paid*	*Value Now*
	G4HC-005	1820	rev. 1					
	G4HC-010	1820	PROOF; rev. 1					
	G4HC-015	1820	PROOF; rev. 1; edge plain					
	G4HC-020	1820	PROOF; rev. 2					
	G4HC-025	1821	rev. 1					
	G4HC-030	1821	rev. 2					
	G4HC-035	1821	PROOF; rev 2					
	G4HC-040	1823	rev. 2					
	G4HC-045	1823	rev. 3					
	G4HC-050	1823	PROOF; rev. 3					
	G4HC-055	1824	obv. 1, rev. 3					
	G4HC-060	1824	PROOF; obv. 1, rev. 3					
	G4HC-065	1824	PROOF in copper; obv. 1, rev. 3; edge plain					
	G4HC-070	1824	obv. 2, rev. 4					
	G4HC-075	1825						
	G4HC-080	1825	PROOF					
	G4HC-085	1825	PROOF; edge plain					

✓	No.	Date	Features	Grade	Purchased From	Date	Price Paid	Value Now
	G4HC-090	1825	PROOF in Barton's metal; edge plain					
	G4HC-095	1826						
	G4HC-100	1826	PROOF					
	G4HC-105	1828						
	G4HC-110	1829						

William IV 1830 – 1837

✓	No.	Date	Features	Grade	Purchased From	Date	Price Paid	Value Now
	W4HC-005	1831	W.W. block caps					
	W4HC-010	1831	PROOF; W.W. block caps; edge plain					
	W4HC-015	1831	PROOF; W.W. in script					
	W4HC-020	1831	PROOF; W.W. in script; edge plain					
	W4HC-025	1831	PROOF; W.W. in script; edge plain; rev. ↓					
	W4HC-030	1834	W.W. block caps					
	W4HC-035	1834	PROOF; W.W. block caps					
	W4HC-040	1834	W.W. in script					
	W4HC-045	1834	PROOF; W.W. in script					
	W4HC-050	1834	PROOF; W.W. in script; edge plain					
	W4HC-055	1835						
	W4HC-060	1836						
	W4HC-065	1836	6 over 5					
	W4HC-070	1836	PROOF; edge plain					
	W4HC-075	1837						

Victoria 1837 – 1901

Young Head

✓	No.	Date	Features	Grade	Purchased From	Date	Price Paid	Value Now
	VYHC-005	1839	obv. 1					
	VYHC-010	1839	PROOF; obv. 1					
	VYHC-015	1839	PROOF; obv. 1; edge plain; rev. ↓					
	VYHC-020	1839	PROOF; obv. 1; edge plain					
	VYHC-025	1839	PROOF; obv. 2; edge plain					
	VYHC-030	1839	PROOF; obv. 3; edge plain; rev. ↓					
	VYHC-035	1839	obv. 4					
	VYHC-040	1839	PROOF; obv. 4					
	VYHC-045	1839	PROOF; obv. 4; edge plain					
	VYHC-050	1840						
	VYHC-055	1841						
	VYHC-060	1842						
	VYHC-065	1843						
	VYHC-070	1844						
	VYHC-075	1844	struck on large flan; edge plain					
	VYHC-080	1845						
	VYHC-085	1846						
	VYHC-088	1846	8 over 1					
	VYHC-090	1848						

Cont.

✓	No.	Date	Features	Grade	Purchased From	Date	Price Paid	Value Now
	VYHC-095	1848	latter 8 over 6					
	VYHC-100	1848	latter 8 over 7					
	VYHC-105	1849	large date					
	VYHC-110	1849	small date					
	VYHC-115	1850						
	VYHC-120	1850	PROOF					
	VYHC-125	1853	PROOF					
	VYHC-130	1862	PROOF					
	VYHC-135	1862	PROOF; edge plain; rev. ↓					
	VYHC-140	1864	PROOF; rev. ↓					
	VYHC-145	1864	PROOF; edge plain; rev. ↓					
	VYHC-150	1874						
	VYHC-155	1874	PROOF					
	VYHC-160	1874	PROOF; edge plain					
	VYHC-165	1874	PROOF in gold; edge plain					
	VYHC-170	1875						
	VYHC-175	1875	PROOF					
	VYHC-180	1875	PROOF; edge plain					
	VYHC-185	1876						
	VYHC-190	1876	6 over 5					
	VYHC-195	1877						
	VYHC-200	1878						
	VYHC-205	1878	PROOF					
	VYHC-210	1879						
	VYHC-215	1879	PROOF; rev. ↓					
	VYHC-220	1879	PROOF; edge plain; rev. ↓					
	VYHC-225	1880						
	VYHC-230	1880	PROOF					
	VYHC-235	1881						
	VYHC-240	1881	PROOF					
	VYHC-245	1881	PROOF; edge plain					
	VYHC-250	1882						
	VYHC-255	1883						
	VYHC-260	1884						
	VYHC-265	1885						
	VYHC-270	1885	PROOF					
	VYHC-275	1886						
	VYHC-280	1886	PROOF					
	VYHC-285	1887						
	VYHC-290	1887	PROOF					

Jubilee Head

✓	No.	Date	Features	Grade	Purchased From	Date	Price Paid	Value Now
	VJHC-295	1887						
	VJHC-300	1887	PROOF					
	VJHC-305	1888						
	VJHC-310	1889						
	VJHC-315	1890						
	VJHC-320	1891						
	VJHC-325	1892						

Old Head

✓	No.	Date	Features	Grade	Purchased From	Date	Price Paid	Value Now
	VOHC-330	1893						
	VOHC-335	1893	PROOF					
	VOHC-340	1894						
	VOHC-345	1895						
	VOHC-350	1896						
	VOHC-355	1897						
	VOHC-360	1898						
	VOHC-365	1899						
	VOHC-370	1900						
	VOHC-375	1901						

Edward VII 1901 – 1910

✓	No.	Date	Features	Grade	Purchased From	Date	Price Paid	Value Now
	E7HC-005	1902						
	E7HC-010	1902	matt PROOF					
	E7HC-015	1903						
	E7HC-020	1904						
	E7HC-025	1905						
	E7HC-030	1906						
	E7HC-035	1907						
	E7HC-040	1908						
	E7HC-045	1909						
	E7HC-050	1910						

George V 1910 – 1936

Sterling Silver Issue

✓	No.	Date	Features	Grade	Purchased From	Date	Price Paid	Value Now
	G5HC-005	1911						
	G5HC-010	1911	PROOF					
	G5HC-015	1912						
	G5HC-020	1913						
	G5HC-025	1914						
	G5HC-030	1915						
	G5HC-035	1916						
	G5HC-040	1917						
	G5HC-045	1918						
	G5HC-050	1919						

50% Silver Issue

✓	No.	Date	Features	Grade	Purchased From	Date	Price Paid	Value Now
	G5HC-055	1920						
	G5HC-060	1921						
	G5HC-065	1922						
	G5HC-070	1923						
	G5HC-075	1924						

Cont.

✓	No.	Date	Features	Grade	Purchased From	Date	Price Paid	Value Now
	G5HC-080	1925						
	G5HC-085	1926						
	G5HC-090	1926	modified effigy					
	G5HC-095	1927						
	G5HC-100	1927	PROOF in nickel					
	G5HC-105	1927	PROOF					
	G5HC-110	1927	PROOF from sandblasted dies					
	G5HC-115	1928						
	G5HC-120	1928	PROOF					
	G5HC-125	1929						
	G5HC-130	1929	PROOF					
	G5HC-135	1930						
	G5HC-140	1930	PROOF					
	G5HC-145	1931						
	G5HC-150	1931	PROOF					
	G5HC-155	1932						
	G5HC-160	1932	PROOF					
	G5HC-165	1933						
	G5HC-170	1933	PROOF					
	G5HC-175	1934						
	G5HC-180	1934	PROOF					
	G5HC-185	1935						
	G5HC-190	1935	PROOF					
	G5HC-195	1936						
	G5HC-200	1936	PROOF					

Edward VIII 1936

✓	No.	Date	Features	Grade	Purchased From	Date	Price Paid	Value Now
	E8HC-005	1937						

George VI 1937 – 1952

50% Silver Issue

✓	No.	Date	Features	Grade	Purchased From	Date	Price Paid	Value Now
	G6HC-005	1937						
	G6HC-010	1937	PROOF					
	G6HC-015	1937	PROOF from sandblasted dies					
	G6HC-020	1938						
	G6HC-025	1938	PROOF					
	G6HC-030	1939						
	G6HC-035	1939	PROOF					
	G6HC-040	1940						
	G6HC-045	1940	PROOF					
	G6HC-050	1941						
	G6HC-055	1941	PROOF					
	G6HC-060	1942						
	G6HC-065	1943						
	G6HC-070	1943	PROOF					

Cont.

✓	No.	Date	Features	Grade	Purchased From	Date	Price Paid	Value Now
	G6HC-075	1944						
	G6HC-080	1945						
	G6HC-085	1945	PROOF					
	G6HC-090	1946						
	G6HC-095	1946	PROOF					

Cupronickel Issue

✓	No.	Date	Features	Grade	Purchased From	Date	Price Paid	Value Now
	G6HC-100	1946	PROOF in cupronickel					
	G6HC-105	1947						
	G6HC-110	1947	PROOF					
	G6HC-115	1948						
	G6HC-120	1948	PROOF					
	G6HC-125	1949						
	G6HC-130	1949	PROOF					
	G6HC-135	1950						
	G6HC-140	1950	PROOF					
	G6HC-145	1950	PROOF from sandblasted dies					
	G6HC-150	1951						
	G6HC-155	1951	PROOF					
	G6HC-160	1951	PROOF from sandblasted dies					
	G6HC-165	1952						

Elizabeth II 1952 –

✓	No.	Date	Features	Grade	Purchased From	Date	Price Paid	Value Now
	EL2HC-005	1953						
	EL2HC-010	1953	PROOF					
	EL2HC-015	1953	PROOF from sandblasted dies					
	EL2HC-020	1954						
	EL2HC-025	1954	PROOF					
	EL2HC-030	1955						
	EL2HC-035	1955	PROOF					
	EL2HC-040	1956						
	EL2HC-045	1956	PROOF					
	EL2HC-050	1957						
	EL2HC-055	1957	PROOF					
	EL2HC-060	1958						
	EL2HC-065	1958	PROOF					
	EL2HC-070	1959						
	EL2HC-075	1959	PROOF					
	EL2HC-080	1960						
	EL2HC-085	1960	PROOF					
	EL2HC-090	1961						
	EL2HC-095	1961	struck from polished blanks					
	EL2HC-100	1961	PROOF					
	EL2HC-105	1962						
	EL2HC-110	1962	PROOF					
	EL2HC-115	1963						
	EL2HC-120	1963	PROOF					

Cont.

✓	No.	Date	Features	*Grade*	*Purchased From*	*Date*	*Price Paid*	*Value Now*
	EL2HC-125	1964						
	EL2HC-130	1964	PROOF					
	EL2HC-135	1965						
	EL2HC-140	1965	PROOF					
	EL2HC-145	1966						
	EL2HC-150	1966	PROOF					
	EL2HC-155	1967						
	EL2HC-160	1967	PROOF					
	EL2HC-165	1970	PROOF					

Florin

Victoria 1837 – 1901

'Godless' Issue

✓	No.	Date	Features	Grade	Purchased From	Date	Price Paid	Value Now
	VGFL-002	1848						
	VGFL-005	1849	WW next to date					
	VGFL-010	1849	WW next to date partially erased					

'Gothic' Issue

✓	No.	Date	Features	Grade	Purchased From	Date	Price Paid	Value Now
	VGFL-015	1851	mdcccli.					
	VGFL-020	1851	PROOF; edge plain; mdcccli.					
	VGFL-025	1851	PROOF; mdcccli.					
	VGFL-030	1852	mdccclii.					
	VGFL-035	1852	2 over 1; mdccclii.					
	VGFL-040	1852	PROOF; mdccclii.					
	VGFL-045	1853	mdcccliii					
	VGFL-050	1853	PROOF; mdcccliii					
	VGFL-055	1854	mdcccliv					
	VGFL-058	1854	ONC TENTH instead of ONE TENTH (rev.); mdcccliv					
	VGFL-060	1855	mdccclv					
	VGFL-065	1856	mdccclvi					
	VGFL-070	1857	mdccclvii					
	VGFL-075	1858	mdccclviii					
	VGFL-080	1859	mdccclix					
	VGFL-085	1859	mdccclix.					
	VGFL-090	1859	m in date is double struck inverted m; mdccclix.					
	VGFL-095	1860	mdccclx.					
	VGFL-100	1862	mdccclxii					
	VGFL-105	1862	PROOF; edge plain; mdccclxii					
	VGFL-110	1863	mdccclxiii					
	VGFL-115	1863	PROOF; edge plain; mdccclxiii					
	VGFL-120	1864	with die number; mdccclxiv					
	VGFL-125	1864	struck on thick flan; with die number; mdccclxiv					
	VGFL-130	1864	PROOF; struck on thick flan; with die number; mdccclxiv					
	VGFL-135	1865	with die number; mdccclxv					
	VGFL-140	1865	with die number; mdccclxv:					
	VGFL-145	1865	with die number; rev. →; mdccclxv:					
	VGFL-150	1866	with die number; mdccclxvi					
	VGFL-155	1866	with die number; mdccclxvi:					
	VGFL-160	1867	with die number; mdccclxvii					
	VGFL-165	1867	PROOF; mdccclxvii					
	VGFL-170	1867	PROOF; edge plain; rev. ↓; mdccclxvii					

✓	No.	Date	Features	Grade	Purchased From	Date	Price Paid	Value Now
	VGFL-175	1867 (1877)	with die number; mdccclxvii					
	VGFL-180	1868	with die number; mdccclxviii					
	VGFL-185	1869	with die number; mdccclxix					
	VGFL-190	1869	PROOF; with die number; mdccclxix					
	VGFL-195	1870	with die number; mdccclxx					
	VGFL-200	1870	PROOF; with die number; mdccclxx					
	VGFL-205	1871	with die number; mdccclxxi					
	VGFL-210	1871	PROOF; with die number; rev. ↓; mdccclxxi					
	VGFL-215	1871	PROOF; with die number; edge plain; rev. ↓; mdccclxxi					
	VGFL-220	1872	with die number; mdccclxxii					
	VGFL-225	1873	with die number; mdccclxxiii					
	VGFL-230	1873	PROOF; with die number; mdccclxxiii					
	VGFL-235	1874	with die number; mdccclxxiv					
	VGFL-240	1874	4 over 3; with die number; mdccclxxiv					
	VGFL-245	1875	with die number; mdccclxxv					
	VGFL-250	1876	with die number; mdccclxxvi					
	VGFL-255	1877	obv. 3; with die number; mdccclxxvii					
	VGFL-260	1877	obv. 4; with die number; mdccclxxvii.					
	VGFL-265	1877	obv. 5; with die number; mdccclxxvii.					
	VGFL-270	1877	obv. 5; mdccclxxvii.					
	VGFL-175 duplicated entry	1877 (1867)	obv. 5; with die number; mdccclxvii (.)					
	VGFL-275	1878	with die number; mdccclxxviii					
	VGFL-280	1878	PROOF; with die number; mdccclxxviii					
	VGFL-285	1879	obv. 3; with die number; mdccclxxix					
	VGFL-290	1879	obv. 3; mdccclxxix					
	VGFL-292	1879	obv. 3; briit over britt (obv.); mdccclxxix					
	VGFL-295	1879	obv. 5; mdccclxxix					
	VGFL-300	1879	obv. 6; mdccclxxix					
	VGFL-305	1879	obv. 6; PROOF; mdccclxxix					
	VGFL-310	1879	obv. 6; PROOF; edge plain; rev. ↓; mdccclxxix					
	VGFL-315	1880	obv. 7; mdccclxxx					
	VGFL-320	1880	obv. 8; mdccclxxx					
	VGFL-325	1880	obv. 8; PROOF; mdccclxxx					
	VGFL-330	1881	mdccclxxxi					
	VGFL-335	1881	mdccclxxri					
	VGFL-340	1881	PROOF; mdccclxxxi					
	VGFL-345	1881	PROOF; edge plain; rev. ↓; mdccclxxxi					
	VGFL-350	1883	mdccclxxxiii					
	VGFL-355	1884	mdccclxxxiv					
	VGFL-360	1885	mdccclxxxv					
	VGFL-365	1885	PROOF; mdccclxxxv					
	VGFL-370	1886	mdccclxxxvi					
	VGFL-375	1886	PROOF; mdccclxxxvi					
	VGFL-380	1887	mdccclxxxvii					
	VGFL-385	1887	PROOF; mdccclxxxvii					

Jubilee Head

✓	No.	Date	Features	Grade	Purchased From	Date	Price Paid	Value Now
	VJFL-390	1887						
	VJFL-395	1887	PROOF					
	VJFL-400	1888						
	VJFL-405	1889						
	VJFL-410	1890						
	VJFL-415	1891						
	VJFL-420	1892						
	VJFL-425	1892	PROOF					

Old Head

✓	No.	Date	Features	Grade	Purchased From	Date	Price Paid	Value Now
	VOFL-430	1893						
	VOFL-435	1893	PROOF					
	VOFL-440	1894						
	VOFL-445	1895						
	VOFL-450	1896						
	VOFL-455	1897						
	VOFL-460	1898						
	VOFL-465	1899						
	VOFL-470	1900						
	VOFL-475	1901						

Edward VII 1901 – 1910

✓	No.	Date	Features	Grade	Purchased From	Date	Price Paid	Value Now
	E7FL-005	1902						
	E7FL-010	1902	matt PROOF					
	E7FL-015	1903						
	E7FL-020	1904						
	E7FL-025	1905						
	E7FL-030	1906						
	E7FL-035	1907						
	E7FL-040	1908						
	E7FL-045	1909						
	E7FL-050	1910						

George V 1910 – 1936

Sterling Silver Issue

✓	No.	Date	Features	Grade	Purchased From	Date	Price Paid	Value Now
	G5FL-005	1911	obv. 1					
	G5FL-010	1911	PROOF					
	G5FL-015	1911	obv. 2					
	G5FL-020	1912						
	G5FL-025	1913						
	G5FL-030	1914						
	G5FL-035	1915						

Cont.

✓	No.	Date	Features	*Grade*	*Purchased From*	*Date*	*Price Paid*	*Value Now*
	G5FL-040	1916						
	G5FL-045	1917						
	G5FL-050	1918						
	G5FL-055	1919						

50% Silver Issue

✓	No.	Date	Features	*Grade*	*Purchased From*	*Date*	*Price Paid*	*Value Now*
	G5FL-060	1920						
	G5FL-065	1921						
	G5FL-070	1922						
	G5FL-075	1922	PROOF in gold					
	G5FL-080	1923						
	G5FL-085	1924						
	G5FL-090	1925						
	G5FL-095	1926						
	G5FL-100	1927	PROOF					
	G5FL-105	1927	PROOF from sandblasted dies					
	G5FL-110	1928						
	G5FL-115	1928	PROOF					
	G5FL-120	1929						
	G5FL-125	1929	PROOF					
	G5FL-130	1930						
	G5FL-135	1930	PROOF					
	G5FL-140	1931						
	G5FL-145	1931	PROOF					
	G5FL-150	1932						
	G5FL-155	1932	PROOF					
	G5FL-160	1933						
	G5FL-165	1933	PROOF					
	G5FL-170	1935						
	G5FL-175	1935	PROOF					
	G5FL-180	1936						
	G5FL-185	1936	PROOF					

Edward VIII 1936

✓	No.	Date	Features	*Grade*	*Purchased From*	*Date*	*Price Paid*	*Value Now*
	E8FL-005	1937						

George VI 1937 – 1952

50% Silver Issue

✓	No.	Date	Features	*Grade*	*Purchased From*	*Date*	*Price Paid*	*Value Now*
	G6FL-005	1937						
	G6FL-010	1937	PROOF					
	G6FL-015	1937	PROOF from sandblasted dies					
	G6FL-020	1938						
	G6FL-025	1938	PROOF					

Cont.

✓	No.	Date	Features	Grade	Purchased From	Date	Price Paid	Value Now
	G6FL-030	1939						
	G6FL-035	1939	PROOF					
	G6FL-040	1940						
	G6FL-045	1940	PROOF					
	G6FL-050	1941						
	G6FL-055	1941	PROOF					
	G6FL-060	1942						
	G6FL-065	1942	PROOF					
	G6FL-070	1943						
	G6FL-075	1944						
	G6FL-080	1944	PROOF					
	G6FL-085	1945						
	G6FL-090	1945	PROOF					
	G6FL-095	1946						
	G6FL-100	1946	PROOF					

Cupronickel Issue

✓	No.	Date	Features	Grade	Purchased From	Date	Price Paid	Value Now
	G6FL-105	1946	PROOF in cupronickel					
	G6FL-110	1947						
	G6FL-115	1947	PROOF					
	G6FL-120	1948						
	G6FL-125	1948	PROOF					
	G6FL-130	1949						
	G6FL-135	1949	PROOF					
	G6FL-140	1950						
	G6FL-145	1950	PROOF					
	G6FL-150	1950	PROOF from sandblasted dies					
	G6FL-155	1951						
	G6FL-160	1951	PROOF					
	G6FL-165	1951	PROOF from sandblasted dies					

Elizabeth II 1952 –

✓	No.	Date	Features	Grade	Purchased From	Date	Price Paid	Value Now
	EL2FL-005	1953						
	EL2FL-010	1953	PROOF					
	EL2FL-015	1953	PROOF from sandblasted dies					
	EL2FL-020	1954						
	EL2FL-025	1954	PROOF					
	EL2FL-030	1955						
	EL2FL-035	1955	PROOF					
	EL2FL-040	1956						
	EL2FL-045	1956	PROOF					
	EL2FL-050	1957						
	EL2FL-055	1957	PROOF					
	EL2FL-060	1958						
	EL2FL-065	1958	PROOF					
	EL2FL-070	1959						
	EL2FL-075	1959	PROOF					

Cont.

✓	No.	Date	Features	*Grade*	*Purchased From*	*Date*	*Price Paid*	*Value Now*
	EL2FL-080	1960						
	EL2FL-085	1960	PROOF					
	EL2FL-090	1961						
	EL2FL-095	1961	PROOF					
	EL2FL-100	1962						
	EL2FL-105	1962	PROOF					
	EL2FL-110	1963						
	EL2FL-115	1963	PROOF					
	EL2FL-120	1964						
	EL2FL-125	1964	PROOF					
	EL2FL-130	1965						
	EL2FL-135	1965	struck in brass or nickel-brass					
	EL2FL-140	1965	PROOF					
	EL2FL-145	1966						
	EL2FL-150	1966	PROOF					
	EL2FL-155	1967						
	EL2FL-160	1967	struck on both sides with rev. design					
	EL2FL-165	1967	PROOF					
	EL2FL-170	1970	PROOF					

Eighteen Pence Bank Token

George III 1760 – 1820

✓	No.	Date	Features	*Grade*	*Purchased From*	*Date*	*Price Paid*	*Value Now*
	G318D-005	1811						
	G318D-010	1811	PROOF					
	G318D-015	1812	small head					
	G318D-020	1812	large head					
	G318D-025	1812	PROOF					
	G318D-030	1812	PROOF; small lettering on rev.					
	G318D-035	1812	PROOF in platinum					
	G318D-040	1813						
	G318D-045	1813	PROOF in platinum					
	G318D-050	1814						
	G318D-055	1815						
	G318D-060	1816						

Shilling

George III 1760 – 1820

✓	No.	Date	Features	*Grade*	*Purchased From*	*Date*	*Price Paid*	*Value Now*
	G3SH-090	1816						
	G3SH-095	1816	PROOF					
	G3SH-100	1816	PROOF; edge plain					
	G3SH-105	1816	PROOF in gold					
	G3SH-110	1817						
	G3SH-112	1817	I of HONI over S (rev.)					
	G3SH-115	1817	PROOF; edge plain					
	G3SH-120	1817	GEOE instead of GEOR (obv.)					
	G3SH-122	1817	RRITT instead of BRITT (obv.)					
	G3SH-125	1818						
	G3SH-130	1819						
	G3SH-135	1819	9 over 8					
	G3SH-140	1820						
	G3SH-142	1820	rev. ↓					
	G3SH-145	1820	I of HONI over S (rev.)					
	G3SH-150	1820	H of HONI over horizontal H					
	G3SH-155	1820	PROOF					

George IV 1820 – 1830

✓	No.	Date	Features	*Grade*	*Purchased From*	*Date*	*Price Paid*	*Value Now*
	G4SH-005	1821						
	G4SH-010	1821	PROOF					
	G4SH-015	1823						
	G4SH-020	1823	PROOF					
	G4SH-025	1824						
	G4SH-030	1824	PROOF					
	G4SH-035	1825	obv. 1, rev. 2					
	G4SH-040	1825	5 over 3; obv. 1, rev. 2					
	G4SH-045	1825	PROOF; obv. 1, rev. 2					
	G4SH-050	1825	obv. 2, rev. 3					
	G4SH-055	1825	I instead of 1 in date; obv. 2, rev. 3					
	G4SH-060	1825	PROOF; obv. 2, rev. 3					
	G4SH-065	1825	PROOF in Barton's metal; edge plain; obv. 2, rev. 3					
	G4SH-070	1826						
	G4SH-075	1826	Roman I in date					
	G4SH-080	1826	PROOF					
	G4SH-085	1826	6 over 2					
	G4SH-090	1827						
	G4SH-095	1829						
	G4SH-100	1829	PROOF					

William IV 1830 – 1837

✓	No.	Date	Features	Grade	Purchased From	Date	Price Paid	Value Now
	W4SH-005	1831	PROOF; edge plain					
	W4SH-010	1831	PROOF					
	W4SH-015	1834						
	W4SH-020	1834	PROOF					
	W4SH-025	1834	PROOF round-top '3' in date					
	W4SH-030	1835						
	W4SH-035	1835	PROOF round-top '3' in date					
	W4SH-040	1836						
	W4SH-045	1836	PROOF round-top '3' in date					
	W4SH-050	1836	PROOF in copper; edge plain					
	W4SH-055	1837						
	W4SH-060	1837	PROOF					

Victoria 1837 – 1901

Young Head

✓	No.	Date	Features	Grade	Purchased From	Date	Price Paid	Value Now
	VYSH-005	1838	obv. 1					
	VYSH-010	1838	PROOF; obv. 1					
	VYSH-015	1839	obv. 1					
	VYSH-020	1839	PROOF; edge plain; obv. 1					
	VYSH-025	1839	PROOF; edge plain; obv. 2					
	VYSH-030	1839	obv. 3					
	VYSH-035	1839	PROOF; obv. 3					
	VYSH-040	1839	PROOF; edge plain; obv. 3					
	VYSH-045	1839	PROOF; edge plain; rev. ↓; obv. 3					
	VYSH-050	1840						
	VYSH-055	1840	PROOF					
	VYSH-060	1841						
	VYSH-065	1842						
	VYSH-070	1842	PROOF					
	VYSH-075	1843						
	VYSH-080	1844						
	VYSH-085	1845						
	VYSH-090	1846						
	VYSH-095	1848	latter 8 over 6					
	VYSH-100	1849						
	VYSH-105	1850						
	VYSH-110	1850	50 over 46 or 49					
	VYSH-115	1851						
	VYSH-120	1851	PROOF					
	VYSH-125	1852						
	VYSH-130	1853						
	VYSH-135	1853	PROOF					
	VYSH-140	1854						
	VYSH-145	1854	4 over 1					
	VYSH-150	1855						

Cont.

✓	No.	Date	Features	*Grade*	*Purchased From*	*Date*	*Price Paid*	*Value Now*
	VYSH-155	1856						
	VYSH-160	1857						
	VYSH-165	1857	inverted G or broken D at end of obv. legend					
	VYSH-170	1857	7 over 5					
	VYSH-175	1858						
	VYSH-178	1858	latter 8 over 6					
	VYSH-180	1858	PROOF					
	VYSH-185	1859						
	VYSH-190	1860						
	VYSH-195	1861						
	VYSH-200	1862						
	VYSH-205	1863						
	VYSH-210	1863	3 over 1					
	VYSH-215	1863	3 over 2					
	VYSH-220	1864	die number above date					
	VYSH-225	1865	die number above date					
	VYSH-230	1866	die number above date					
	VYSH-235	1866	die number above date BBITANNIAR instead of BRITANNIAR (obv.)					
	VYSH-240	1867	die number above date; obv. 3					
	VYSH-245	1867	PROOF					
	VYSH-250	1867	PROOF; edge plain					
	VYSH-255	1867	die number above date; obv. 4					
	VYSH-260	1868	die number above date					
	VYSH-265	1869	die number above date					
	VYSH-270	1870	die number above date					
	VYSH-275	1871	die number above date					
	VYSH-280	1871	PROOF die number above date					
	VYSH-285	1871	PROOF; edge plain; rev. ↓ die number above date					
	VYSH-290	1872	die number above date					
	VYSH-295	1873	die number above date					
	VYSH-300	1874	die number above date					
	VYSH-305	1875	die number above date					
	VYSH-310	1876	die number above date					
	VYSH-315	1877	die number above date					
	VYSH-320	1878	die number above date; obv. 4					
	VYSH-322	1878	die number above date; obv. 5					
	VYSH-325	1878	PROOF; die number above date					
	VYSH-330	1879	die number above date					
	VYSH-335	1879	PROOF die number above date					
	VYSH-340	1879						
	VYSH-345	1879	PROOF; edge plain; rev. ↓					
	VYSH-350	1880						
	VYSH-355	1880	PROOF					
	VYSH-360	1880	PROOF; edge plain					
	VYSH-365	1881						
	VYSH-370	1881	PROOF					
	VYSH-375	1881	PROOF; edge plain					
	VYSH-380	1882						
	VYSH-385	1883						

Cont.

✓	No.	Date	Features	Grade	Purchased From	Date	Price Paid	Value Now
	VYSH-390	1884						
	VYSH-395	1884	PROOF					
	VYSH-400	1885						
	VYSH-405	1885	PROOF					
	VYSH-410	1886						
	VYSH-415	1886	PROOF					
	VYSH-420	1887						
	VYSH-425	1887	PROOF					

Jubilee Head

✓	No.	Date	Features	Grade	Purchased From	Date	Price Paid	Value Now
	VJSH-430	1887						
	VJSH-435	1887	PROOF					
	VJSH-440	1888						
	VJSH-445	1888	last 8 over 7					
	VJSH-450	1889						
	VJSH-455	1889	small head					
	VJSH-460	1889	large head					
	VJSH-465	1889	PROOF					
	VJSH-470	1890						
	VJSH-475	1891						
	VJSH-480	1891	PROOF					
	VJSH-485	1892						

Old Head

✓	No.	Date	Features	Grade	Purchased From	Date	Price Paid	Value Now
	VOSH-490	1893	obv. 8					
	VOSH-495	1893	obv. 9					
	VOSH-500	1893	PROOF					
	VOSH-505	1894	obv. 8					
	VOSH-510	1894	obv. 9					
	VOSH-515	1895	rev. 5					
	VOSH-520	1895	rev. 6					
	VOSH-525	1896	rev. 5					
	VOSH-530	1896	rev. 6					
	VOSH-535	1897						
	VOSH-540	1898						
	VOSH-545	1899						
	VOSH-550	1900						
	VOSH-555	1901						

Edward VII 1901 – 1910

✓	No.	Date	Features	Grade	Purchased From	Date	Price Paid	Value Now
	E7SH-005	1902						
	E7SH-010	1902	matt PROOF					
	E7SH-015	1903						
	E7SH-020	1904						
	E7SH-025	1905						

Cont.

✓	No.	Date	Features	*Grade*	*Purchased From*	*Date*	*Price Paid*	*Value Now*
	E7SH-030	1906						
	E7SH-035	1907						
	E7SH-040	1908						
	E7SH-045	1909						
	E7SH-050	1910						

George V 1910 – 1936

Sterling Silver Issue

✓	No.	Date	Features	*Grade*	*Purchased From*	*Date*	*Price Paid*	*Value Now*
	G5SH-005	1911						
	G5SH-010	1911	PROOF					
	G5SH-015	1912						
	G5SH-020	1913						
	G5SH-025	1914						
	G5SH-030	1915						
	G5SH-035	1916						
	G5SH-040	1917						
	G5SH-045	1918						
	G5SH-050	1919						

50% Silver Issue

✓	No.	Date	Features	*Grade*	*Purchased From*	*Date*	*Price Paid*	*Value Now*
	G5SH-055	1920						
	G5SH-060	1921						
	G5SH-065	1922						
	G5SH-070	1923						
	G5SH-075	1923	struck in nickel					
	G5SH-080	1924						
	G5SH-085	1924	struck in nickel					
	G5SH-090	1925						
	G5SH-095	1926						
	G5SH-100	1926	modified effigy					
	G5SH-105	1927	rev. 1					
	G5SH-110	1927	rev. 2					
	G5SH-115	1927	PROOF					
	G5SH-120	1927	PROOF from sandblasted dies					
	G5SH-125	1928						
	G5SH-130	1928	PROOF					
	G5SH-135	1929						
	G5SH-140	1929	PROOF					
	G5SH-145	1930						
	G5SH-150	1930	PROOF					
	G5SH-155	1931						
	G5SH-160	1931	PROOF					
	G5SH-165	1932						
	G5SH-170	1932	PROOF					
	G5SH-175	1933						
	G5SH-180	1933	PROOF					

Cont.

✓	No.	Date	Features	Grade	Purchased From	Date	Price Paid	Value Now
	G5SH-185	1934						
	G5SH-190	1934	PROOF					
	G5SH-195	1935						
	G5SH-200	1935	PROOF					
	G5SH-205	1936						
	G5SH-210	1936	PROOF					

Edward VIII 1936

✓	No.	Date	Features	Grade	Purchased From	Date	Price Paid	Value Now
	E8SH-005	1937						

George VI 1937 – 1952

50% Silver Issue

✓	No.	Date	Features	Grade	Purchased From	Date	Price Paid	Value Now
	G6SH-005	1937	English					
	G6SH-010	1937	English PROOF					
	G6SH-015	1937	English PROOF from sandblasted dies					
	G6SH-020	1937	Scottish					
	G6SH-025	1937	Scottish PROOF					
	G6SH-030	1937	Scottish PROOF from sandblasted dies					
	G6SH-035	1938	English					
	G6SH-040	1938	English PROOF					
	G6SH-045	1938	Scottish					
	G6SH-050	1938	Scottish PROOF					
	G6SH-055	1939	English					
	G6SH-060	1939	English PROOF					
	G6SH-065	1939	Scottish					
	G6SH-070	1939	Scottish PROOF					
	G6SH-075	1940	English					
	G6SH-080	1940	English PROOF					
	G6SH-085	1940	Scottish					
	G6SH-090	1940	Scottish PROOF					
	G6SH-095	1941	English					
	G6SH-100	1941	English PROOF					
	G6SH-105	1941	Scottish					
	G6SH-110	1941	Scottish PROOF					
	G6SH-115	1942	English					
	G6SH-120	1942	Scottish					
	G6SH-125	1943	English					
	G6SH-128	1943	English; rev. ↓					
	G6SH-130	1943	Scottish					
	G6SH-135	1944	English					
	G6SH-140	1944	English PROOF					
	G6SH-145	1944	Scottish					
	G6SH-150	1944	Scottish PROOF					
	G6SH-155	1945	English					

Cont.

✓	No.	Date	Features	Grade	Purchased From	Date	Price Paid	Value Now
	G6SH-160	1945	English PROOF					
	G6SH-165	1945	Scottish					
	G6SH-170	1945	Scottish PROOF					
	G6SH-175	1946	English					
	G6SH-180	1946	English PROOF					
	G6SH-185	1946	English PROOF in cupronickel					
	G6SH-190	1946	Scottish					
	G6SH-195	1946	Scottish PROOF					

Cupronickel Issue

✓	No.	Date	Features	Grade	Purchased From	Date	Price Paid	Value Now
	G6SH-200	1947	English					
	G6SH-205	1947	English struck in 0.5 silver					
	G6SH-210	1947	English PROOF					
	G6SH-215	1947	Scottish					
	G6SH-220	1947	Scottish PROOF					
	G6SH-225	1948	English					
	G6SH-230	1948	English PROOF					
	G6SH-235	1948	Scottish					
	G6SH-240	1948	Scottish PROOF					
	G6SH-245	1949	English					
	G6SH-250	1949	English PROOF					
	G6SH-255	1949	Scottish					
	G6SH-260	1949	Scottish PROOF					
	G6SH-265	1950	English					
	G6SH-270	1950	English PROOF					
	G6SH-275	1950	English PROOF from sandblasted dies					
	G6SH-280	1950	Scottish					
	G6SH-285	1950	Scottish PROOF					
	G6SH-290	1950	Scottish PROOF from sandblasted dies					
	G6SH-295	1951	English					
	G6SH-300	1951	English PROOF					
	G6SH-305	1951	English PROOF from sandblasted dies					
	G6SH-310	1951	Scottish					
	G6SH-315	1951	Scottish PROOF					
	G6SH-320	1951	Scottish PROOF from sandblasted dies					
	G6SH-325	1952	English PROOF					
	G6SH-330	1952	English PROOF in nickel					

Elizabeth II 1952 –

✓	No.	Date	Features	Grade	Purchased From	Date	Price Paid	Value Now
	EL2SH-005	1953	English					
	EL2SH-010	1953	'double headed'					
	EL2SH-015	1953	English PROOF					
	EL2SH-020	1953	English PROOF from sandblasted dies					
	EL2SH-025	1953	Scottish					
	EL2SH-030	1953	Scottish PROOF					

Cont.

✓	No.	Date	Features	*Grade*	*Purchased From*	*Date*	*Price Paid*	*Value Now*
	EL2SH-035	1953	Scottish PROOF from sandblasted dies					
	EL2SH-040	1954	English					
	EL2SH-045	1954	English PROOF					
	EL2SH-050	1954	Scottish					
	EL2SH-055	1954	Scottish PROOF					
	EL2SH-060	1955	English					
	EL2SH-065	1955	English PROOF					
	EL2SH-070	1955	Scottish					
	EL2SH-075	1955	Scottish PROOF					
	EL2SH-080	1956	English					
	EL2SH-085	1956	English PROOF					
	EL2SH-090	1956	Scottish					
	EL2SH-095	1956	Scottish PROOF					
	EL2SH-100	1957	English					
	EL2SH-105	1957	English PROOF					
	EL2SH-110	1957	Scottish					
	EL2SH-115	1957	Scottish PROOF					
	EL2SH-120	1958	English					
	EL2SH-125	1958	English PROOF					
	EL2SH-130	1958	Scottish					
	EL2SH-135	1958	Scottish PROOF					
	EL2SH-140	1959	English					
	EL2SH-145	1959	English PROOF					
	EL2SH-150	1959	Scottish					
	EL2SH-155	1959	Scottish PROOF					
	EL2SH-160	1960	English					
	EL2SH-165	1960	English PROOF					
	EL2SH-170	1960	Scottish					
	EL2SH-175	1960	Scottish PROOF					
	EL2SH-180	1961	English					
	EL2SH-185	1961	English PROOF					
	EL2SH-190	1961	Scottish					
	EL2SH-195	1961	Scottish PROOF					
	EL2SH-200	1962	English					
	EL2SH-205	1962	English PROOF					
	EL2SH-210	1962	Scottish					
	EL2SH-215	1962	Scottish PROOF					
	EL2SH-220	1963	English					
	EL2SH-225	1963	English PROOF					
	EL2SH-230	1963	Scottish					
	EL2SH-235	1963	Scottish PROOF					
	EL2SH-240	1964	English					
	EL2SH-245	1964	English PROOF					
	EL2SH-250	1964	Scottish					
	EL2SH-255	1964	Scottish PROOF					
	EL2SH-260	1965	English					
	EL2SH-265	1965	English PROOF					
	EL2SH-270	1965	Scottish					
	EL2SH-275	1965	Scottish PROOF					
	EL2SH-280	1966	English					
	EL2SH-285	1966	English PROOF					

Cont.

✓	No.	Date	Features	*Grade*	*Purchased From*	*Date*	*Price Paid*	*Value Now*
	EL2SH-290	1966	Scottish					
	EL2SH-295	1966	Scottish rev. ↓					
	EL2SH-300	1966	Scottish PROOF					
	EL2SH-305	1970	English PROOF					
	EL2SH-310	1970	Scottish PROOF					

Sixpence

George III 1760 – 1820

✓	No.	Date	Features	*Grade*	*Purchased From*	*Date*	*Price Paid*	*Value Now*
	G36D-025	1816						
	G36D-030	1816	PROOF in gold					
	G36D-035	1817						
	G36D-040	1817	PROOF					
	G36D-045	1817	PROOF; edge plain					
	G36D-050	1818						
	G36D-055	1818	PROOF					
	G36D-060	1819						
	G36D-065	1819	8 in date very small					
	G36D-070	1819	PROOF; 9 not over 8					
	G36D-075	1819	PROOF; 9 over 8					
	G36D-080	1820						
	G36D-085	1820	1 in date inverted					
	G36D-088	1820	I of HONI over S (rev.)					
	G36D-090	1820	PROOF					

George IV 1820 – 1830

✓	No.	Date	Features	*Grade*	*Purchased From*	*Date*	*Price Paid*	*Value Now*
	G46D-005	1821						
	G46D-010	1821	BBITANNIAR instead of BRITANNIAR (obv.)					
	G46D-015	1821	PROOF					
	G46D-020	1824						
	G46D-025	1824	PROOF					
	G46D-030	1825						
	G46D-035	1825	PROOF					
	G46D-040	1826	obv. 1, rev. 2					
	G46D-045	1826	rev. ↓; obv. 1, rev. 2					
	G46D-050	1826	PROOF; obv. 1, rev. 2					
	G46D-055	1826	obv. 2, rev. 3					
	G46D-060	1826	PROOF; obv. 2, rev. 3					
	G46D-065	1826	PROOF in pewter; struck on thick flan; obv. 2, rev. 3					
	G46D-070	1827						
	G46D-075	1828						
	G46D-080	1829						
	G46D-085	1829	PROOF					

William IV 1830 – 1837

✓	No.	Date	Features	*Grade*	*Purchased From*	*Date*	*Price Paid*	*Value Now*
	W46D-005	1831						
	W46D-010	1831	PROOF					

✓	No.	Date	Features	Grade	Purchased From	Date	Price Paid	Value Now
	W46D-015	1831	PROOF on thin flan; edge plain					
	W46D-020	1831	PROOF; edge plain					
	W46D-025	1831	PROOF in palladium					
	W46D-030	1834						
	W46D-035	1834	PROOF					
	W46D-040	1834	PROOF; round-top 3 in date					
	W46D-045	1835						
	W46D-050	1835	PROOF; round-top 3 in date					
	W46D-055	1836						
	W46D-060	1836	PROOF; round-top 3 in date					
	W46D-065	1837						
	W46D-070	1837	PROOF					

Victoria 1837 – 1901

Young Head

✓	No.	Date	Features	Grade	Purchased From	Date	Price Paid	Value Now
	VY6D-005	1838						
	VY6D-010	1838	PROOF					
	VY6D-015	1839						
	VY6D-020	1839	PROOF; edge plain					
	VY6D-025	1839	PROOF; edge plain; rev. ↓					
	VY6D-030	1839	PROOF; rev. ↓; obv. as 1880–87					
	VY6D-035	1840						
	VY6D-040	1841						
	VY6D-045	1842						
	VY6D-050	1842	each 'I' in VICTORIA is a numeral '1' (obv.)					
	VY6D-055	1843						
	VY6D-060	1844						
	VY6D-065	1844	large 44 in date					
	VY6D-070	1845						
	VY6D-075	1846						
	VY6D-080	1848						
	VY6D-085	1848	8 over 6					
	VY6D-090	1848	8 over 7					
	VY6D-095	1850						
	VY6D-100	1851						
	VY6D-105	1852						
	VY6D-110	1853						
	VY6D-115	1853	PROOF					
	VY6D-120	1854						
	VY6D-125	1855						
	VY6D-130	1855	PROOF					
	VY6D-135	1856						
	VY6D-140	1857						
	VY6D-145	1858						
	VY6D-150	1858	PROOF					
	VY6D-155	1859						
	VY6D-160	1859	9 over 8					

Cont.

✓	No.	Date	Features	*Grade*	*Purchased From*	*Date*	*Price Paid*	*Value Now*
	VY6D-165	1860						
	VY6D-170	1860	6 over indeterminate figure					
	VY6D-175	1862						
	VY6D-180	1863						
	VY6D-185	1864	die number above date					
	VY6D-190	1865	die number above date					
	VY6D-195	1866	die number above date					
	VY6D-200	1866						
	VY6D-205	1867	die number above date					
	VY6D-210	1867	die number above date PROOF					
	VY6D-215	1868	die number above date					
	VY6D-220	1869	die number above date					
	VY6D-225	1869	die number above date PROOF					
	VY6D-230	1870	die number above date					
	VY6D-235	1870	die number above date PROOF; edge plain					
	VY6D-240	1871	die number above date					
	VY6D-245	1871						
	VY6D-250	1871	die number above date PROOF; rev. ↓					
	VY6D-255	1871	die number above date PROOF; edge plain					
	VY6D-260	1871	PROOF					
	VY6D-265	1872	die number above date					
	VY6D-270	1873	die number above date					
	VY6D-275	1874	die number above date					
	VY6D-280	1875	die number above date					
	VY6D-285	1876	die number above date					
	VY6D-290	1877	die number above date					
	VY6D-295	1877						
	VY6D-300	1878	die number above date					
	VY6D-305	1878	die number above date PROOF					
	VY6D-310	1878	8 over 7 die number above date					
	VY6D-315	1878	DRITANNIAR instead of BRITANNIAR (obv.) die number 6 above date					
	VY6D-320	1879	die number above date					
	VY6D-325	1879						
	VY6D-330	1879	PROOF					
	VY6D-335	1879	PROOF; edge plain; rev. ↓					
	VY6D-340	1879	larger border beads					
	VY6D-345	1880	larger border beads; obv. 2					
	VY6D-350	1880	obv. 3					
	VY6D-355	1880	PROOF; obv. 3					
	VY6D-360	1881						
	VY6D-365	1881	PROOF					
	VY6D-370	1881	PROOF; edge plain					
	VY6D-375	1882						
	VY6D-380	1883						
	VY6D-385	1884						
	VY6D-390	1885						
	VY6D-395	1885	PROOF					
	VY6D-400	1886						

Cont.

✓	No.	Date	Features	Grade	Purchased From	Date	Price Paid	Value Now
	VY6D-405	1886	PROOF					
	VY6D-410	1887						
	VY6D-415	1887	PROOF					

Jubilee Head

✓	No.	Date	Features	Grade	Purchased From	Date	Price Paid	Value Now
	VJ6D-420	1887	obv. 4					
	VJ6D-425	1887	obv. 5					
	VJ6D-430	1887	PROOF					
	VJ6D-435	1887						
	VJ6D-440	1887	PROOF					
	VJ6D-445	1888						
	VJ6D-450	1888	PROOF					
	VJ6D-455	1889						
	VJ6D-460	1890						
	VJ6D-465	1890	PROOF					
	VJ6D-470	1891						
	VJ6D-475	1892						
	VJ6D-480	1893						

Old Head

✓	No.	Date	Features	Grade	Purchased From	Date	Price Paid	Value Now
	VO6D-485	1893						
	VO6D-490	1893	PROOF					
	VO6D-495	1894						
	VO6D-500	1895						
	VO6D-505	1896						
	VO6D-510	1897						
	VO6D-515	1898						
	VO6D-520	1899						
	VO6D-525	1900						
	VO6D-530	1901						

Edward VII 1901 – 1910

✓	No.	Date	Features	Grade	Purchased From	Date	Price Paid	Value Now
	E76D-005	1902						
	E76D-010	1902	matt PROOF					
	E76D-015	1903						
	E76D-020	1904						
	E76D-025	1905						
	E76D-030	1906						
	E76D-035	1907						
	E76D-040	1908						
	E76D-045	1909						
	E76D-050	1910						

George V 1910 – 1936

Sterling Silver Issue

✓	No.	Date	Features	*Grade*	*Purchased From*	*Date*	*Price Paid*	*Value Now*
	G56D-005	1911						
	G56D-010	1911	PROOF					
	G56D-015	1912						
	G56D-020	1913						
	G56D-025	1914						
	G56D-030	1915						
	G56D-035	1916						
	G56D-040	1917						
	G56D-045	1918						
	G56D-050	1919						
	G56D-055	1920						

50% Silver Issue

✓	No.	Date	Features	*Grade*	*Purchased From*	*Date*	*Price Paid*	*Value Now*
	G56D-060	1920						
	G56D-065	1921						
	G56D-070	1922						
	G56D-075	1923						
	G56D-080	1924						
	G56D-085	1925						
	G56D-090	1926						
	G56D-095	1926	modified effigy					
	G56D-100	1927	rev. 1					
	G56D-105	1927	struck in nickel; rev. 1					
	G56D-110	1927	PROOF; rev. 2					
	G56D-115	1927	PROOF from sandblasted dies; rev. 2					
	G56D-120	1928						
	G56D-125	1928	PROOF					
	G56D-130	1929						
	G56D-135	1929	PROOF					
	G56D-140	1930						
	G56D-145	1930	PROOF					
	G56D-150	1931						
	G56D-155	1931	PROOF					
	G56D-160	1932						
	G56D-165	1932	PROOF					
	G56D-170	1933						
	G56D-175	1933	PROOF					
	G56D-180	1934						
	G56D-185	1934	PROOF					
	G56D-190	1935						
	G56D-195	1935	PROOF					
	G56D-200	1936						
	G56D-205	1936	PROOF					

Edward VIII 1936

✓	No.	Date	Features	Grade	Purchased From	Date	Price Paid	Value Now
	E86D-005	1937						

George VI 1937 – 1952

50% Silver Issue

✓	No.	Date	Features	Grade	Purchased From	Date	Price Paid	Value Now
	G66D-005	1937						
	G66D-010	1937	PROOF					
	G66D-015	1937	PROOF from sandblasted dies					
	G66D-020	1938						
	G66D-025	1938	PROOF					
	G66D-030	1939						
	G66D-035	1939	PROOF					
	G66D-040	1940						
	G66D-045	1940	PROOF					
	G66D-050	1941						
	G66D-055	1941	PROOF					
	G66D-060	1942						
	G66D-065	1943						
	G66D-070	1943	PROOF					
	G66D-075	1944						
	G66D-080	1944	PROOF					
	G66D-085	1945						
	G66D-090	1945	PROOF					
	G66D-095	1946						
	G66D-100	1946	PROOF					

Cupronickel Issue

✓	No.	Date	Features	Grade	Purchased From	Date	Price Paid	Value Now
	G66D-105	1946	PROOF in cupronickel					
	G66D-110	1947						
	G66D-115	1947	PROOF					
	G66D-120	1948						
	G66D-125	1948	PROOF					
	G66D-130	1949						
	G66D-135	1949	PROOF					
	G66D-140	1950						
	G66D-145	1950	PROOF					
	G66D-150	1950	PROOF from sandblasted dies					
	G66D-155	1951						
	G66D-160	1951	PROOF					
	G66D-165	1951	PROOF from sandblasted dies					
	G66D-170	1952						
	G66D-175	1952	PROOF					

Elizabeth II 1952 –

✓	No.	Date	Features	*Grade*	*Purchased From*	*Date*	*Price Paid*	*Value Now*
	EL26D-005	1953						
	EL26D-010	1953	PROOF					
	EL26D-015	1953	PROOF from sandblasted dies					
	EL26D-020	1954						
	EL26D-025	1954	PROOF					
	EL26D-030	1955						
	EL26D-035	1955	PROOF					
	EL26D-040	1956						
	EL26D-045	1956	PROOF					
	EL26D-050	1957						
	EL26D-052	1957	rev. ↓					
	EL26D-055	1957	PROOF					
	EL26D-060	1958						
	EL26D-065	1958	PROOF					
	EL26D-070	1959						
	EL26D-075	1959	PROOF					
	EL26D-080	1960						
	EL26D-085	1960	PROOF					
	EL26D-090	1961						
	EL26D-095	1961	PROOF					
	EL26D-100	1962						
	EL26D-105	1962	PROOF					
	EL26D-110	1963						
	EL26D-115	1963	PROOF					
	EL26D-120	1964						
	EL26D-125	1964	PROOF					
	EL26D-130	1965						
	EL26D-135	1965	PROOF					
	EL26D-140	1966						
	EL26D-145	1966	struck in bronze					
	EL26D-150	1966	PROOF					
	EL26D-155	1966	error obverse as Mauritius quarter rupee					
	EL26D-160	1967						
	EL26D-165	1967	PROOF					
	EL26D-170	1970	PROOF					

Maundy Fourpence

George III 1760 – 1820

✓	No.	Date	Features	Grade	Purchased From	Date	Price Paid	Value Now
	G34M-080	1817						
	G34M-085	1818						
	G34M-090	1820						

George IV 1820 – 1830

✓	No.	Date	Features	Grade	Purchased From	Date	Price Paid	Value Now
	G44M-005	1822–30						

William IV 1830 – 1837

✓	No.	Date	Features	Grade	Purchased From	Date	Price Paid	Value Now
	W44M-005	1831–37						

Victoria 1837 – 1901

✓	No.	Date	Features	Grade	Purchased From	Date	Price Paid	Value Now
	VY4M-005	1838–87						
	VJ4M-010	1888–92						
	VO4M-015	1893–1901						

Edward VII 1901 – 1910

✓	No.	Date	Features	Grade	Purchased From	Date	Price Paid	Value Now
	E74M-005	1902–1910						

George V 1910 – 1936

✓	No.	Date	Features	Grade	Purchased From	Date	Price Paid	Value Now
	G54M-005	1911–27						
	G54M-010	1928–29						
	G54M-015	1930–36						

George VI 1937 – 1952

✓	No.	Date	Features	Grade	Purchased From	Date	Price Paid	Value Now
	G64M-005	1937–48						
	G64M-010	1949–52						

Elizabeth II 1952 –

✓	No.	Date	Features	*Grade*	*Purchased From*	*Date*	*Price Paid*	*Value Now*
	EL24M-005	1953						
	EL24M-010	1954–97						

Groat

William IV 1830 – 1837

✓	No.	Date	Features	*Grade*	*Purchased From*	*Date*	*Price Paid*	*Value Now*
	W44D-005	1836						
	W44D-010	1836	PROOF					
	W44D-015	1836	PROOF; edge plain					
	W44D-020	1836	PROOF in gold					
	W44D-025	1836	PROOF on thin flan					
	W44D-030	1837						
	W44D-035	1837	PROOF					
	W44D-040	1837	PROOF; edge plain					

Victoria 1837 – 1901

✓	No.	Date	Features	*Grade*	*Purchased From*	*Date*	*Price Paid*	*Value Now*
	VY4D-005	1837	PROOF or pattern; rev. ↓					
	VY4D-010	1837	PROOF or pattern; edge plain					
	VY4D-015	1838						
	VY4D-020	1838	PROOF; edge plain					
	VY4D-025	1838	latter 8 over horizontal 8					
	VY4D-030	1839						
	VY4D-035	1839	PROOF; edge plain					
	VY4D-040	1839	PROOF; edge plain; rev. ↓					
	VY4D-045	1840						
	VY4D-050	1841	latter 1 over inverted 1					
	VY4D-055	1842						
	VY4D-060	1842	PROOF; edge plain					
	VY4D-065	1842	2 over 1					
	VY4D-070	1843						
	VY4D-075	1843	4 over 5					
	VY4D-080	1844						
	VY4D-085	1845						
	VY4D-090	1846						
	VY4D-095	1847	7 over 6					
	VY4D-100	1848						
	VY4D-105	1848	latter 8 over 6					
	VY4D-110	1848	latter 8 over 7					
	VY4D-115	1849						
	VY4D-120	1849	9 over 8					
	VY4D-125	1851						
	VY4D-130	1852						
	VY4D-135	1853						
	VY4D-140	1853	PROOF					
	VY4D-145	1853	PROOF; edge plain					
	VY4D-150	1854						
	VY4D-155	1855						
	VY4D-160	1857	PROOF					

✓	No.	Date	Features	*Grade*	*Purchased From*	*Date*	*Price Paid*	*Value Now*
	VY4D-165	1862	PROOF					
	VY4D-170	1862	PROOF; edge plain					
	VJ4D-175	1888						
	VJ4D-180	1888	PROOF					

Silver Threepence

George III 1760 – 1820

✓	No.	Date	Features	*Grade*	*Purchased From*	*Date*	*Price Paid*	*Value Now*
	G33M-080	1817						
	G33M-085	1818						
	G33M-090	1820						

George IV 1820 – 1830

✓	No.	Date	Features	*Grade*	*Purchased From*	*Date*	*Price Paid*	*Value Now*
	G43M-005	1822						
	G43M-010	1823–30						

William IV 1830 – 1837

Maundy issue

✓	No.	Date	Features	*Grade*	*Purchased From*	*Date*	*Price Paid*	*Value Now*
	W43M-005	1831–37						

Non-Maundy issue

✓	No.	Date	Features	*Grade*	*Purchased From*	*Date*	*Price Paid*	*Value Now*
	W43D-005	1834						
	W43D-010	1835						
	W43D-015	1836						
	W43D-020	1837						

Victoria 1837 – 1901

Maundy issue

✓	No.	Date	Features	*Grade*	*Purchased From*	*Date*	*Price Paid*	*Value Now*
	VY3M-005	1838–87						
	VJ3M-010	1888–92						
	VO3M-015	1893–1901						

Non-Maundy issue: Young Head

✓	No.	Date	Features	*Grade*	*Purchased From*	*Date*	*Price Paid*	*Value Now*
	VY3D-005	1838						
	VY3D-010	1839						
	VY3D-015	1840						
	VY3D-020	1841						
	VY3D-025	1842						
	VY3D-030	1843						
	VY3D-035	1844						

✓	No.	Date	Features	Grade	Purchased From	Date	Price Paid	Value Now
	VY3D-040	1845						
	VY3D-045	1846						
	VY3D-050	1849						
	VY3D-055	1850						
	VY3D-060	1851						
	VY3D-062	1851	8 under 5 (i.e. appears as 1551)					
	VY3D-065	1852						
	VY3D-070	1853						
	VY3D-075	1854						
	VY3D-080	1855						
	VY3D-085	1856						
	VY3D-090	1857						
	VY3D-095	1858						
	VY3D-098	1858	latter 8 over 6					
	VY3D-100	1858	BRITANNIAB instead of BRITANNIAR (obv.)					
	VY3D-105	1859						
	VY3D-110	1860						
	VY3D-115	1861						
	VY3D-120	1862						
	VY3D-125	1863						
	VY3D-130	1864						
	VY3D-135	1865						
	VY3D-140	1866						
	VY3D-145	1867						
	VY3D-150	1868						
	VY3D-155	1868	RRITANNIAR instead of BRITANNIAR (obv.)					
	VY3D-160	1869						
	VY3D-165	1870						
	VY3D-170	1871						
	VY3D-175	1872						
	VY3D-180	1873						
	VY3D-185	1874						
	VY3D-190	1875						
	VY3D-195	1876						
	VY3D-200	1877						
	VY3D-205	1878						
	VY3D-208	1878	B of BRITANNIAR under R (obv.)					
	VY3D-210	1879						
	VY3D-215	1879	PROOF; rev. ↓					
	VY3D-220	1880						
	VY3D-225	1881						
	VY3D-230	1882						
	VY3D-235	1883						
	VY3D-240	1884						
	VY3D-245	1885						
	VY3D-250	1886						
	VY3D-255	1887						
	VY3D-260	1887	PROOF					

Non-Maundy issue: Jubilee Head

✓	No.	Date	Features	Grade	Purchased From	Date	Price Paid	Value Now
	VJ3D-265	1887						
	VJ3D-270	1887	PROOF					
	VJ3D-275	1888						
	VJ3D-280	1889						
	VJ3D-285	1890						
	VJ3D-290	1891						
	VJ3D-295	1892						
	VJ3D-300	1893						

Non-Maundy issue: Old Head

✓	No.	Date	Features	Grade	Purchased From	Date	Price Paid	Value Now
	VO3D-305	1893						
	VO3D-310	1893	PROOF					
	VO3D-315	1894						
	VO3D-320	1895						
	VO3D-325	1896						
	VO3D-330	1897						
	VO3D-335	1898						
	VO3D-340	1899						
	VO3D-345	1900						
	VO3D-350	1901						

Edward VII 1901 – 1910

Maundy issue

✓	No.	Date	Features	Grade	Purchased From	Date	Price Paid	Value Now
	E73M-005	1902–10						

Non-Maundy issue

✓	No.	Date	Features	Grade	Purchased From	Date	Price Paid	Value Now
	E73D-005	1902						
	E73D-010	1903						
	E73D-015	1904						
	E73D-020	1905						
	E73D-025	1906						
	E73D-030	1907						
	E73D-035	1908						
	E73D-040	1909						
	E73D-045	1910						

George V 1910 – 1936

Maundy issue

✓	No.	Date	Features	Grade	Purchased From	Date	Price Paid	Value Now
	G53M-005	1911–27						

Cont.

✓	No.	Date	Features	Grade	Purchased From	Date	Price Paid	Value Now
	G53M-010	1928–29						
	G53M-015	1930–36						

Non-Maundy issue: Sterling Silver Issue

✓	No.	Date	Features	Grade	Purchased From	Date	Price Paid	Value Now
	G53D-005	1911						
	G53D-010	1912						
	G53D-015	1913						
	G53D-020	1914						
	G53D-025	1915						
	G53D-030	1916						
	G53D-035	1917						
	G53D-040	1918						
	G53D-045	1919						

Non-Maundy issue: 50% Silver Issue

✓	No.	Date	Features	Grade	Purchased From	Date	Price Paid	Value Now
	G53D-050	1920						
	G53D-055	1921						
	G53D-060	1922						
	G53D-065	1925						
	G53D-070	1926						
	G53D-075	1926	modified effigy					
	G53D-080	1927	PROOF					
	G53D-085	1927	PROOF from sandblasted dies					
	G53D-090	1928						
	G53D-095	1928	PROOF					
	G53D-100	1930						
	G53D-105	1930	PROOF					
	G53D-110	1931						
	G53D-115	1931	PROOF					
	G53D-120	1932						
	G53D-125	1932	PROOF					
	G53D-130	1933						
	G53D-135	1933	PROOF					
	G53D-140	1934						
	G53D-145	1934	PROOF					
	G53D-150	1935						
	G53D-155	1935	PROOF					
	G53D-160	1936						
	G53D-165	1936	PROOF					

Edward VIII 1936

✓	No.	Date	Features	Grade	Purchased From	Date	Price Paid	Value Now
	E83D-005	1937						

George VI 1937 – 1952

Maundy issue

✓	No.	Date	Features	*Grade*	*Purchased From*	*Date*	*Price Paid*	*Value Now*
	G63M-005	1937–48						
	G63M-010	1949–52						

Non-Maundy issue

✓	No.	Date	Features	*Grade*	*Purchased From*	*Date*	*Price Paid*	*Value Now*
	G63D-005	1937						
	G63D-010	1937	PROOF					
	G63D-015	1937	PROOF from sandblasted dies					
	G63D-020	1938						
	G63D-025	1938	PROOF					
	G63D-030	1939						
	G63D-035	1939	PROOF					
	G63D-040	1940						
	G63D-045	1940	PROOF					
	G63D-050	1941						
	G63D-055	1941	PROOF					
	G63D-060	1942						
	G63D-065	1943						
	G63D-070	1944						
	G63D-075	1945						

Elizabeth II 1952 –

Maundy issue

✓	No.	Date	Features	*Grade*	*Purchased From*	*Date*	*Price Paid*	*Value Now*
	EL23M-005	1953						
	EL23M-010	1954–1997						

Brass Threepence

Edward VIII 1936

✓	No.	Date	Features	Grade	Purchased From	Date	Price Paid	Value Now
	E83DB-005	1937						

George VI 1937 – 1952

✓	No.	Date	Features	Grade	Purchased From	Date	Price Paid	Value Now
	G63DB-005	1937						
	G63DB-010	1937	PROOF					
	G63DB-015	1937	PROOF from sandblasted dies					
	G63DB-020	1937	struck on round nickel blank for Hong Kong 10 cents					
	G63DB-025	1938						
	G63DB-030	1938	PROOF					
	G63DB-035	1939						
	G63DB-040	1939	PROOF					
	G63DB-045	1940						
	G63DB-050	1940	PROOF					
	G63DB-055	1941						
	G63DB-060	1941	rounded corners					
	G63DB-065	1941	PROOF					
	G63DB-070	1942	rounded corners					
	G63DB-075	1942	PROOF; rounded corners					
	G63DB-080	1943	rounded corners					
	G63DB-085	1943	PROOF; rounded corners					
	G63DB-090	1944	rounded corners					
	G63DB-095	1944	PROOF; rounded corners					
	G63DB-100	1945	rounded corners					
	G63DB-105	1945	PROOF; rounded corners					
	G63DB-110	1946	rounded corners					
	G63DB-115	1946	PROOF; rounded corners					
	G63DB-120	1948	rounded corners					
	G63DB-125	1948						
	G63DB-130	1948	PROOF					
	G63DB-135	1949	rounded corners					
	G63DB-140	1949	PROOF; rounded corners					
	G63DB-145	1950						
	G63DB-150	1950	PROOF					
	G63DB-155	1950	PROOF from sandblasted dies					
	G63DB-160	1951						
	G63DB-165	1951	PROOF					
	G63DB-170	1951	PROOF from sandblasted dies					
	G63DB-175	1952						
	G63DB-180	1952	PROOF					

Elizabeth II 1952 –

✓	No.	Date	Features	*Grade*	*Purchased From*	*Date*	*Price Paid*	*Value Now*
	EL23DB-005	1953						
	EL23DB-010	1953	PROOF					
	EL23DB-015	1953	PROOF from sandblasted dies					
	EL23DB-020	1954						
	EL23DB-025	1954	PROOF					
	EL23DB-030	1955						
	EL23DB-035	1955	PROOF					
	EL23DB-040	1956						
	EL23DB-045	1956	PROOF					
	EL23DB-050	1957						
	EL23DB-055	1957	PROOF					
	EL23DB-060	1958						
	EL23DB-065	1958	struck in cupronickel					
	EL23DB-070	1958	PROOF					
	EL23DB-075	1959						
	EL23DB-080	1959	PROOF					
	EL23DB-085	1960						
	EL23DB-090	1960	PROOF					
	EL23DB-095	1961						
	EL23DB-098	1961	struck on blank for Hong Kong 10 cents					
	EL23DB-100	1961	PROOF					
	EL23DB-105	1962						
	EL23DB-110	1962	PROOF					
	EL23DB-115	1963						
	EL23DB-120	1963	PROOF					
	EL23DB-125	1964						
	EL23DB-130	1964	PROOF					
	EL23DB-135	1965						
	EL23DB-140	1965	PROOF					
	EL23DB-145	1966						
	EL23DB-150	1966	struck in cupronickel					
	EL23DB-155	1966	PROOF					
	EL23DB-160	1967						
	EL23DB-165	1967	PROOF					
	EL23DB-170	1970	PROOF					
	EL23DB-175		'double headed' error					

Silver Twopence

All are Maundy issues unless stated.

George III 1760 – 1820

✓	No.	Date	Features	Grade	Purchased From	Date	Price Paid	Value Now
	G32M-070	1817						
	G32M-075	1818						
	G32M-080	1820						

George IV 1820 – 1830

✓	No.	Date	Features	Grade	Purchased From	Date	Price Paid	Value Now
	G42M-005	1822–30						

William IV 1830 – 1837

✓	No.	Date	Features	Grade	Purchased From	Date	Price Paid	Value Now
	W42M-005	1831–37						

Victoria 1837 – 1901

✓	No.	Date	Features	Grade	Purchased From	Date	Price Paid	Value Now
	VY2M-005	1838–87						
	VJ2M-010	1888–92						
	VO2M-015	1893–1901						

✓	No.	Date	Features	Grade	Purchased From	Date	Price Paid	Value Now
	VY2M-020	1838	Non-Maundy issue					
	VY2M-025	1843	Non-Maundy issue					
	VY2M-030	1848	Non-Maundy issue					

Edward VII 1901 – 1910

✓	No.	Date	Features	Grade	Purchased From	Date	Price Paid	Value Now
	E72M-005	1902–10						

George V 1910 – 1936

✓	No.	Date	Features	Grade	Purchased From	Date	Price Paid	Value Now
	G52M-005	1911–27						
	G52M-010	1928–29						
	G52M-015	1930–36						

George VI 1937 – 1952

✓	No.	Date	Features	*Grade*	*Purchased From*	*Date*	*Price Paid*	*Value Now*
	G62M-005	1937–48						
	G62M-010	1949–52						

Elizabeth II 1952 –

✓	No.	Date	Features	*Grade*	*Purchased From*	*Date*	*Price Paid*	*Value Now*
	EL22M-005	1953						
	EL22M-010	1954–97						

Three Halfpence

William IV 1830 – 1837

✓	No.	Date	Features	*Grade*	*Purchased From*	*Date*	*Price Paid*	*Value Now*
	W43HD-005	1834						
	W43HD-010	1835						
	W43HD-015	1835	5 over 4					
	W43HD-020	1836						
	W43HD-025	1837						

Victoria 1837 – 1901

✓	No.	Date	Features	*Grade*	*Purchased From*	*Date*	*Price Paid*	*Value Now*
	VY3HD-005	1838						
	VY3HD-010	1839						
	VY3HD-015	1840						
	VY3HD-020	1841						
	VY3HD-025	1842						
	VY3HD-030	1843						
	VY3HD-035	1843	PROOF					
	VY3HD-040	1843	43 over 34					
	VY3HD-045	1843	43 over 34; PROOF					
	VY3HD-050	1860						
	VY3HD-055	1862						
	VY3HD-060	1862	PROOF					
	VY3HD-065	1870	PROOF or PATTERN					

Silver Penny

George III 1760 – 1820

✓	No.	Date	Features	Grade	Purchased From	Date	Price Paid	Value Now
	G31M-075	1817						
	G31M-080	1818						
	G31M-085	1820						

George IV 1820 – 1830

✓	No.	Date	Features	Grade	Purchased From	Date	Price Paid	Value Now
	G41M-005	1822–30						

William IV 1830 – 1837

✓	No.	Date	Features	Grade	Purchased From	Date	Price Paid	Value Now
	W41M-005	1831–37						

Victoria 1837 – 1901

✓	No.	Date	Features	Grade	Purchased From	Date	Price Paid	Value Now
	VY1M-005	1838–87						
	VJ1M-010	1888–92						
	VO1M-015	1893–1901						

Edward VII 1901 – 1910

✓	No.	Date	Features	Grade	Purchased From	Date	Price Paid	Value Now
	E71M-005	1902–10						

George V 1910 – 1936

✓	No.	Date	Features	Grade	Purchased From	Date	Price Paid	Value Now
	G51M-005	1911–27						
	G51M-010	1928–29						
	G51M-015	1930–36						

George VI 1937 – 1952

✓	No.	Date	Features	Grade	Purchased From	Date	Price Paid	Value Now
	G61M-005	1937–48						
	G61M-010	1949–52						

Elizabeth II 1952 –

✓	No.	Date	Features	*Grade*	*Purchased From*	*Date*	*Price Paid*	*Value Now*
	EL21M-005	1953						
	EL21M-010	1954–97						

Copper/Bronze Penny

George IV 1820 – 1830

✓	No.	Date	Features	*Grade*	*Purchased From*	*Date*	*Price Paid*	*Value Now*
	G41D-005	1825						
	G41D-010	1825	PROOF					
	G41D-015	1826	rev. 1					
	G41D-020	1826	PROOF; rev. 1					
	G41D-025	1826	bronzed PROOF; rev. 1					
	G41D-030	1826	rev. 2					
	G41D-035	1826	bronzed PROOF; rev. 2					
	G41D-040	1826	rev. 3					
	G41D-045	1826	PROOF; rev. 3					
	G41D-050	1826	bronzed PROOF; rev. 3					
	G41D-055	1827						

William IV 1830 – 1837

✓	No.	Date	Features	*Grade*	*Purchased From*	*Date*	*Price Paid*	*Value Now*
	W41D-005	1831	WW on truncation					
	W41D-010	1831	no initials on truncation					
	W41D-015	1831	bronzed PROOF					
	W41D-020	1831	bronzed PROOF; rev. ↓					
	W41D-025	1834						
	W41D-030	1836						
	W41D-035	1837						

Victoria 1837 – 1901

Copper Issue

✓	No.	Date	Features	*Grade*	*Purchased From*	*Date*	*Price Paid*	*Value Now*
	VY1D-005	1839	bronzed PROOF					
	VY1D-010	1841	no colon after REG					
	VY1D-015	1841	colon after REG					
	VY1D-020	1841	colon after REG; PROOF					
	VY1D-025	1841	colon after REG; bronzed PROOF					
	VY1D-030	1841	colon after REG; PROOF in silver					
	VY1D-035	1843	no colon after REG					
	VY1D-040	1843	colon after REG					
	VY1D-045	1844						
	VY1D-050	1845						
	VY1D-055	1846						
	VY1D-060	1846	near colon					
	VY1D-065	1847						
	VY1D-070	1847	near colon					
	VY1D-075	1848						
	VY1D-080	1848	8 over 6					

✓	No.	Date	Features	Grade	Purchased From	Date	Price Paid	Value Now
	VY1D-085	1848	8 over 7					
	VY1D-090	1849						
	VY1D-095	1851						
	VY1D-100	1851	near colon					
	VY1D-105	1853						
	VY1D-110	1853	PROOF					
	VY1D-115	1853	bronzed PROOF rev. ↓					
	VY1D-120	1853	near colon; plain trident head					
	VY1D-125	1854						
	VY1D-130	1854	near colon; plain trident head					
	VY1D-135	1854	PROOF; near colon; plain trident head					
	VY1D-140	1854	near colon; plain trident head 4 over 3					
	VY1D-145	1855						
	VY1D-150	1855	near colon; plain trident head					
	VY1D-155	1856						
	VY1D-160	1856	near colon; plain trident head					
	VY1D-165	1856	near colon; plain trident head PROOF					
	VY1D-170	1857						
	VY1D-175	1857	near colon; plain trident head					
	VY1D-180	1857	near colon; plain trident head small date					
	VY1D-185	1858	obv. 1					
	VY1D-190	1858	small date; obv. 1					
	VY1D-192	1858	small date; latter 8 over 6; obv. 1					
	VY1D-195	1858	latter 8 over 7; obv. 1					
	VY1D-200	1858	obv. 2					
	VY1D-205	1859						
	VY1D-210	1859	small date					
	VY1D-215	1859	PROOF					
	VY1D-220	1860	60 altered from 59					
	VY1D-225	1860	60 altered from 59 rev. ↓					

Bronze Issue; Young Head

✓	No.	Date	Features	Grade	Purchased From	Date	Price Paid	Value Now
	VY1D-230	1860	obv. 3, rev. 2					
	VY1D-235	1860	rev. ↓; obv. 3, rev. 2					
	VY1D-240	1860	PROOF; obv. 3, rev. 2					
	VY1D-245	1860	bronzed PROOF in copper; obv. 3, rev. 2					
	VY1D-250	1860	bronzed PROOF in copper on thick flan; obv. 3, rev. 2					
	VY1D-255	1860	PROOF in silver on thick flan; obv. 3, rev. 2					
	VY1D-260	1860	PROOF in gold; obv. 3, rev. 2					
	VY1D-265	1860	obv. 3, rev. 3					
	VY1D-270	1860	obv. 4, rev. 2					
	VY1D-275	1860	obv. 4, rev. 3					
	VY1D-280	1860	on thick flan; obv. 4, rev. 3					
	VY1D-285	1860	on very thick flan; obv. 4, rev. 3					
	VY1D-290	1860	PROOF; obv. 4, rev. 3					

Cont.

✓	No.	Date	Features	Grade	Purchased From	Date	Price Paid	Value Now
	VY1D-295	1860	obv. 4, rev. 4					
	VY1D-300	1860	obv. 5, rev. 3					
	VY1D-305	1860	obv. 6, rev. 3					
	VY1D-310	1861	obv. 4, rev. 3					
	VY1D-315	1861	obv. 4, rev. 5					
	VY1D-320	1861	obv. 5, rev. 3					
	VY1D-325	1861	on thick flan; obv. 5, rev. 3					
	VY1D-330	1861	obv. 5, rev. 5					
	VY1D-335	1861	obv. 6, rev. 3					
	VY1D-340	1861	6 over 8; obv. 6, rev. 3					
	VY1D-345	1861	PROOF; obv. 6, rev. 3					
	VY1D-350	1861	obv. 6, rev. 5					
	VY1D-355	1861	8 over 6; obv. 6, rev. 5					
	VY1D-360	1861	PROOF; obv. 6, rev. 5					
	VY1D-365	1861	PROOF in gold; rev. ↓; obv. 6, rev. 5					
	VY1D-370	1861	PROOF in silver on thin flan; obv. 6, rev. 5					
	VY1D-375	1861	PROOF in silver on thick flan; obv. 6, rev. 5					
	VY1D-380	1861	PROOF in copper; obv. 6, rev. 5					
	VY1D-385	1862	obv. 4					
	VY1D-390	1862	obv. 6					
	VY1D-392	1862	B of BRITT over R (obv.); obv. 6					
	VY1D-395	1862	8 over 6; obv. 6					
	VY1D-400	1862	date numerals from halfpenny die; obv. 6					
	VY1D-405	1862	PROOF; obv. 6					
	VY1D-410	1863						
	VY1D-415	1863	die number 2 below date					
	VY1D-420	1863	die number 3 below date					
	VY1D-425	1863	die number 4 below date					
	VY1D-430	1863	PROOF					
	VY1D-435	1864						
	VY1D-440	1865						
	VY1D-445	1865	5 over 3					
	VY1D-450	1866						
	VY1D-455	1867						
	VY1D-460	1867	PROOF					
	VY1D-465	1867	bronzed PROOF in copper					
	VY1D-470	1868						
	VY1D-475	1868	PROOF					
	VY1D-480	1868	PROOF in copper					
	VY1D-485	1868	PROOF in cupronickel					
	VY1D-490	1869						
	VY1D-495	1870						
	VY1D-500	1871						
	VY1D-505	1872						
	VY1D-510	1872	PROOF; rev. ↓					
	VY1D-515	1873						
	VY1D-520	1874	obv. 6					
	VY1D-525	1874	narrow date; obv. 6					
	VY1D-530	1874	H below date; obv. 6					

Cont.

✓	No.	Date	Features	*Grade*	*Purchased From*	*Date*	*Price Paid*	*Value Now*
	VY1D-535	1874	H below date; narrow date; obv. 6					
	VY1D-540	1874	obv. 7					
	VY1D-545	1874	narrow date; obv. 7					
	VY1D-550	1874	H below date; obv. 7					
	VY1D-555	1874	H below date; narrow date; obv. 7					
	VY1D-560	1874	PROOF; H below date; narrow date; obv. 7					
	VY1D-565	1875						
	VY1D-570	1875	narrow date					
	VY1D-575	1875	PROOF; narrow date					
	VY1D-580	1875	PROOF in cupronickel					
	VY1D-585	1875	PROOF on thick flan					
	VY1D-590	1875	H below date					
	VY1D-595	1875	PROOF; H below date					
	VY1D-600	1876	H below date					
	VY1D-605	1876	H below date; narrow date					
	VY1D-610	1876	PROOF; H below date; narrow date					
	VY1D-615	1877	narrow date					
	VY1D-620	1877						
	VY1D-625	1877	PROOF					
	VY1D-630	1877	PROOF in cupronickel					
	VY1D-635	1878						
	VY1D-640	1878	PROOF					
	VY1D-645	1879						
	VY1D-650	1879	PROOF					
	VY1D-655	1879	narrow date					
	VY1D-660	1880						
	VY1D-665	1880	PROOF					
	VY1D-670	1881						
	VY1D-675	1881	PROOF					
	VY1D-680	1881	H below date					
	VY1D-685	1881	PROOF; H below date					
	VY1D-690	1882						
	VY1D-695	1882	H below date					
	VY1D-700	1882	H below date; 2 over 1					
	VY1D-705	1882	PROOF; H below date					
	VY1D-710	1883						
	VY1D-715	1883	PROOF					
	VY1D-720	1884						
	VY1D-725	1884	PROOF					
	VY1D-730	1885						
	VY1D-735	1885	PROOF					
	VY1D-740	1886						
	VY1D-745	1886	PROOF					
	VY1D-750	1887						
	VY1D-755	1887	PROOF					
	VY1D-760	1888						
	VY1D-765	1888	both 'I's in VICTORIA have no top left serif					
	VY1D-770	1889						
	VY1D-775	1889	PROOF					
	VY1D-780	1890						

Cont.

✓	No.	Date	Features	Grade	Purchased From	Date	Price Paid	Value Now
	VY1D-785	1890	PROOF					
	VY1D-790	1891						
	VY1D-795	1891	PROOF					
	VY1D-800	1892						
	VY1D-805	1892	PROOF					
	VY1D-810	1893						
	VY1D-815	1893	PROOF					
	VY1D-820	1894						
	VY1D-825	1894	PROOF					

Old Head

✓	No.	Date	Features	Grade	Purchased From	Date	Price Paid	Value Now
	VO1D-830	1895	rev. 6					
	VO1D-835	1895	PROOF; rev. 6					
	VO1D-840	1895	rev. 7					
	VO1D-845	1895	PROOF; rev. 7					
	VO1D-850	1896						
	VO1D-855	1896	PROOF					
	VO1D-860	1897	rev. 7					
	VO1D-865	1897	rev. 8					
	VO1D-870	1898						
	VO1D-875	1899						
	VO1D-880	1900						
	VO1D-885	1900	PROOF					
	VO1D-890	1901						
	VO1D-895	1901	PROOF					

Edward VII 1901 – 1910

✓	No.	Date	Features	Grade	Purchased From	Date	Price Paid	Value Now
	E71D-005	1902	'Low Tide'.					
	E71D-010	1902						
	E71D-015	1903						
	E71D-020	1904						
	E71D-025	1905						
	E71D-030	1906						
	E71D-035	1907						
	E71D-040	1908						
	E71D-045	1908	matt PROOF on thick flan					
	E71D-050	1909						
	E71D-055	1910						

George V 1910 – 1936

✓	No.	Date	Features	Grade	Purchased From	Date	Price Paid	Value Now
	G51D-005	1911						
	G51D-010	1912						
	G51D-015	1912	H to left of date					
	G51D-020	1913						

Cont.

✓	No.	Date	Features	Grade	Purchased From	Date	Price Paid	Value Now
	G51D-025	1914						
	G51D-030	1915						
	G51D-035	1916						
	G51D-040	1917						
	G51D-045	1918						
	G51D-050	1918	H to left of date					
	G51D-055	1918	KN to left of date					
	G51D-060	1919						
	G51D-065	1919	H to left of date					
	G51D-070	1919	KN to left of date					
	G51D-075	1920						
	G51D-080	1921						
	G51D-085	1922						
	G51D-090	1922						
	G51D-095	1926						
	G51D-100	1926	PROOF					
	G51D-105	1926	modified effigy					
	G51D-110	1926	PROOF					
	G51D-115	1927						
	G51D-120	1927	PROOF					
	G51D-125	1928						
	G51D-130	1928	PROOF					
	G51D-135	1929						
	G51D-140	1929	PROOF					
	G51D-145	1930						
	G51D-150	1930	PROOF					
	G51D-155	1931						
	G51D-160	1931	PROOF					
	G51D-165	1932						
	G51D-170	1932	PROOF					
	G51D-175	1933	artificially darkened at mint (?)					
	G51D-178	1933	PROOF; artificially darkened at mint (?)					
	G51D-180	1934	artificially darkened at mint					
	G51D-185	1934	PROOF					
	G51D-190	1935	artificially darkened at mint					
	G51D-195	1935						
	G51D-200	1935	PROOF					
	G51D-205	1936						
	G51D-210	1936	PROOF					

Edward VIII 1936

✓	No.	Date	Features	Grade	Purchased From	Date	Price Paid	Value Now
	E81D-005	1937						

George VI 1937 – 1952

✓	No.	Date	Features	Grade	Purchased From	Date	Price Paid	Value Now
	G61D-005	1937						

Cont.

✓	No.	Date	Features	Grade	Purchased From	Date	Price Paid	Value Now
	G61D-010	1937	PROOF					
	G61D-015	1937	PROOF from sandblasted dies					
	G61D-020	1938						
	G61D-025	1938	PROOF					
	G61D-030	1939						
	G61D-035	1939	PROOF					
	G61D-040	1940						
	G61D-045	1940	PROOF					
	G61D-050	1944	most artificially darkened at mint					
	G61D-055	1944	PROOF; artificially darkened at mint					
	G61D-060	1945	most artificially darkened at mint					
	G61D-065	1945	PROOF; artificially darkened at mint					
	G61D-070	1946	most artificially darkened at mint					
	G61D-075	1946	PROOF; artificially darkened at mint					
	G61D-080	1947						
	G61D-085	1947	PROOF					
	G61D-090	1948						
	G61D-095	1948	PROOF					
	G61D-100	1949						
	G61D-105	1949	PROOF					
	G61D-110	1950						
	G61D-115	1950	PROOF					
	G61D-120	1950	PROOF from sandblasted dies					
	G61D-125	1951						
	G61D-130	1951	PROOF					
	G61D-135	1951	PROOF from sandblasted dies					

Elizabeth II 1952 –

✓	No.	Date	Features	Grade	Purchased From	Date	Price Paid	Value Now
	EL21D-005	1953	obv. 1					
	EL21D-010	1953	PROOF; obv. 2					
	EL21D-015	1953	obv. 2					
	EL21D-020	1953	PROOF; obv. 2					
	EL21D-025	1953	PROOF from sandblasted dies; obv. 2					
	EL21D-030	1954						
	EL21D-035	1961						
	EL21D-040	1961	PROOF					
	EL21D-045	1962						
	EL21D-048	1962	rev. →					
	EL21D-050	1962	struck on heavy flan					
	EL21D-055	1962	PROOF					
	EL21D-060	1963						
	EL21D-065	1963	PROOF					
	EL21D-070	1964						
	EL21D-075	1964	struck without collar in cupronickel					
	EL21D-080	1964	PROOF					
	EL21D-085	1965						
	EL21D-090	1965	struck in gold					
	EL21D-095	1965	struck in cupronickel					

Cont.

✓	No.	Date	Features	*Grade*	*Purchased From*	*Date*	*Price Paid*	*Value Now*
	EL21D-100	1966						
	EL21D-105	1966	struck in cupronickel					
	EL21D-110	1966	obv. of Jersey penny					
	EL21D-115	1967						
	EL21D-120	1967	struck on thin flan					
	EL21D-125	1967	struck on heavy flan					
	EL21D-130	1967	struck in nickel-brass					
	EL21D-135	1970	PROOF					

Halfpenny

George IV 1820 – 1830

✓	No.	Date	Features	*Grade*	*Purchased From*	*Date*	*Price Paid*	*Value Now*
	G4HD-005	1825						
	G4HD-010	1825	PROOF					
	G4HD-015	1826	rev. 1					
	G4HD-020	1826	PROOF; rev. 1					
	G4HD-025	1826	bronzed PROOF; rev. 1					
	G4HD-030	1826	rev. 2					
	G4HD-035	1826	PROOF; rev. 2					
	G4HD-040	1826	bronzed PROOF; rev. 2					
	G4HD-045	1827						

William IV 1830 – 1837

✓	No.	Date	Features	*Grade*	*Purchased From*	*Date*	*Price Paid*	*Value Now*
	W4HD-005	1831						
	W4HD-010	1831	Bronzed PROOF					
	W4HD-015	1831	Bronzed PROOF; rev. ↓					
	W4HD-020	1834						
	W4HD-025	1837						

Victoria 1837 – 1901

Copper Issue

✓	No.	Date	Features	*Grade*	*Purchased From*	*Date*	*Price Paid*	*Value Now*
	VYHD-005	1838						
	VYHD-010	1839	PROOF					
	VYHD-015	1839	PROOF rev. ↓					
	VYHD-020	1841						
	VYHD-025	1841	rev. ↓					
	VYHD-030	1841	Bronzed PROOF					
	VYHD-035	1841	PROOF in silver on thick flan					
	VYHD-040	1843						
	VYHD-045	1844						
	VYHD-050	1845						
	VYHD-055	1846						
	VYHD-060	1847						
	VYHD-065	1848	8 not over 7					
	VYHD-070	1848	8 over 7					
	VYHD-075	1851						
	VYHD-080	1852						
	VYHD-085	1853						
	VYHD-090	1853	3 over 2					
	VYHD-095	1853	PROOF					
	VYHD-100	1853	Bronzed PROOF; rev. ↓					

✓	No.	Date	Features	Grade	Purchased From	Date	Price Paid	Value Now
	VYHD-105	1854						
	VYHD-110	1855						
	VYHD-115	1856						
	VYHD-120	1857						
	VYHD-125	1858						
	VYHD-130	1858	latter 8 over 6					
	VYHD-135	1858	latter 8 over 7					
	VYHD-140	1859						
	VYHD-145	1859	9 over 8					
	VYHD-150	1860						

Bronze Issue; Young Head

✓	No.	Date	Features	Grade	Purchased From	Date	Price Paid	Value Now
	VYHD-155	1860	obv. 2, rev. 2					
	VYHD-160	1860	PROOF; obv. 2, rev. 2					
	VYHD-165	1860	Bronzed PROOF; obv. 2, rev. 2					
	VYHD-170	1860	obv. 3, rev. 2					
	VYHD-175	1860	obv. 3, rev. 3					
	VYHD-180	1860	PROOF; obv. 3, rev. 3					
	VYHD-185	1860	Bronzed PROOF; obv. 3, rev. 3					
	VYHD-190	1861						
	VYHD-195	1861	HALP instead of HALF (rev.)					
	VYHD-200	1861	6 over 8					
	VYHD-205	1861	PROOF					
	VYHD-210	1861	Bronzed PROOF					
	VYHD-215	1861	PROOF in brass					
	VYHD-220	1861	PROOF in cupronickel					
	VYHD-225	1861	PROOF in silver					
	VYHD-230	1861	PROOF in gold; rev. ↓					
	VYHD-235	1862						
	VYHD-240	1862	'A' to left of lighthouse (rev.)					
	VYHD-245	1862	'B' to left of lighthouse (rev.)					
	VYHD-250	1862	'C' to left of lighthouse (rev.)					
	VYHD-255	1862	PROOF					
	VYHD-260	1863						
	VYHD-265	1863	PROOF					
	VYHD-270	1864						
	VYHD-275	1864	PROOF					
	VYHD-280	1865						
	VYHD-285	1865	5 over 3					
	VYHD-290	1866						
	VYHD-295	1866	PROOF					
	VYHD-300	1867						
	VYHD-305	1867	PROOF; rev. ↓					
	VYHD-310	1867	PROOF in copper					
	VYHD-315	1868						
	VYHD-320	1868	PROOF					
	VYHD-325	1868	PROOF in copper					
	VYHD-330	1868	PROOF in cupronickel					
	VYHD-335	1869						

Cont.

✓	No.	Date	Features	Grade	Purchased From	Date	Price Paid	Value Now
	VYHD-340	1870						
	VYHD-345	1871						
	VYHD-350	1872						
	VYHD-355	1872	PROOF in brass					
	VYHD-360	1873						
	VYHD-365	1874	obv. 3					
	VYHD-370	1874	narrow date; obv. 3					
	VYHD-375	1874	obv. 4					
	VYHD-380	1874	narrow date; obv. 4					
	VYHD-385	1874	narrow date 'H' below date; obv. 4					
	VYHD-390	1874	narrow date 'H' below date struck on thick flan; obv. 4					
	VYHD-395	1874	narrow date 'H' below date PROOF; obv. 4					
	VYHD-400	1875						
	VYHD-405	1875	'H' below date					
	VYHD-410	1875	'H' below date struck on thick flan					
	VYHD-415	1875	'H' below date PROOF					
	VYHD-420	1876	'H' below date					
	VYHD-425	1876	'H' below date struck on thick flan					
	VYHD-430	1876	'H' below date PROOF					
	VYHD-435	1877						
	VYHD-440	1877	PROOF					
	VYHD-445	1878						
	VYHD-450	1878	PROOF					
	VYHD-455	1879						
	VYHD-460	1880						
	VYHD-465	1880	PROOF					
	VYHD-470	1881						
	VYHD-475	1881	PROOF; obv. 4					
	VYHD-480	1881	'H' below date					
	VYHD-485	1881	PROOF; obv. 5					
	VYHD-490	1882	'H' below date					
	VYHD-495	1882	'H' below date PROOF					
	VYHD-500	1883	obv. 4					
	VYHD-505	1883	PROOF; obv. 4					
	VYHD-510	1883	obv. 5					
	VYHD-515	1884						
	VYHD-520	1884	PROOF					
	VYHD-525	1885						
	VYHD-530	1885	PROOF					
	VYHD-535	1886						
	VYHD-540	1886	PROOF					
	VYHD-545	1887						
	VYHD-550	1887	PROOF					
	VYHD-555	1888						
	VYHD-560	1889						
	VYHD-565	1889	9 over 8					
	VYHD-570	1889	9 over 8 PROOF					
	VYHD-575	1890						
	VYHD-580	1890	PROOF					
	VYHD-585	1891						

Cont.

✓	No.	Date	Features	Grade	Purchased From	Date	Price Paid	Value Now
	VYHD-590	1891	PROOF					
	VYHD-595	1892						
	VYHD-600	1892	PROOF					
	VYHD-605	1893						
	VYHD-610	1893	PROOF					
	VYHD-615	1894						
	VYHD-620	1894	PROOF					

Old Head

✓	No.	Date	Features	Grade	Purchased From	Date	Price Paid	Value Now
	VOHD-625	1895						
	VOHD-630	1895	PROOF					
	VOHD-635	1896						
	VOHD-640	1896	PROOF					
	VOHD-645	1897						
	VOHD-650	1897						
	VOHD-655	1898						
	VOHD-660	1899						
	VOHD-665	1900						
	VOHD-670	1900	PROOF					
	VOHD-675	1901						
	VOHD-680	1901	PROOF					

Edward VII 1901 – 1910

✓	No.	Date	Features	Grade	Purchased From	Date	Price Paid	Value Now
	E7HD-005	1902	'Low Tide'					
	E7HD-010	1902						
	E7HD-015	1903						
	E7HD-020	1904						
	E7HD-025	1905						
	E7HD-030	1906						
	E7HD-035	1907						
	E7HD-040	1908						
	E7HD-045	1909						
	E7HD-050	1910						

George V 1910 – 1936

✓	No.	Date	Features	Grade	Purchased From	Date	Price Paid	Value Now
	G5HD-005	1911						
	G5HD-010	1912						
	G5HD-015	1913						
	G5HD-020	1914						
	G5HD-025	1915						
	G5HD-030	1916						
	G5HD-035	1917						
	G5HD-040	1918						
	G5HD-045	1919						

Cont.

✓	No.	Date	Features	*Grade*	*Purchased From*	*Date*	*Price Paid*	*Value Now*
	G5HD-050	1920						
	G5HD-055	1921						
	G5HD-060	1922						
	G5HD-065	1923						
	G5HD-070	1924						
	G5HD-075	1925	obv. 1, rev. 1					
	G5HD-080	1925	obv. 2, rev. 2					
	G5HD-085	1926						
	G5HD-090	1926	PROOF					
	G5HD-095	1927						
	G5HD-100	1927	PROOF					
	G5HD-105	1928						
	G5HD-110	1928	PROOF					
	G5HD-115	1929						
	G5HD-120	1929	PROOF					
	G5HD-125	1930						
	G5HD-130	1930	PROOF					
	G5HD-135	1931						
	G5HD-140	1931	PROOF					
	G5HD-145	1932						
	G5HD-150	1932	PROOF					
	G5HD-155	1933						
	G5HD-160	1933	PROOF					
	G5HD-165	1934						
	G5HD-170	1934	PROOF					
	G5HD-175	1935						
	G5HD-180	1935	PROOF					
	G5HD-185	1936						
	G5HD-190	1936	PROOF					

Edward VIII 1936

✓	No.	Date	Features	*Grade*	*Purchased From*	*Date*	*Price Paid*	*Value Now*
	E8HD-005	1937						

George VI 1937 – 1952

✓	No.	Date	Features	*Grade*	*Purchased From*	*Date*	*Price Paid*	*Value Now*
	G6HD-005	1937						
	G6HD-010	1937	PROOF					
	G6HD-015	1937	PROOF from sandblasted dies					
	G6HD-020	1938						
	G6HD-025	1938	PROOF					
	G6HD-030	1939						
	G6HD-035	1939	PROOF					
	G6HD-040	1940						
	G6HD-045	1940	PROOF					
	G6HD-050	1941						
	G6HD-055	1941	PROOF					
	G6HD-060	1942						

Cont.

✓	No.	Date	Features	Grade	Purchased From	Date	Price Paid	Value Now
	G6HD-065	1942	PROOF					
	G6HD-070	1943						
	G6HD-075	1943	PROOF					
	G6HD-080	1944						
	G6HD-085	1944	PROOF					
	G6HD-090	1945						
	G6HD-095	1945	PROOF					
	G6HD-100	1946						
	G6HD-105	1946	PROOF					
	G6HD-110	1947						
	G6HD-115	1947	PROOF					
	G6HD-120	1948						
	G6HD-125	1948	PROOF					
	G6HD-130	1949						
	G6HD-135	1949	PROOF					
	G6HD-140	1950						
	G6HD-145	1950	PROOF					
	G6HD-150	1950	PROOF from sandblasted dies					
	G6HD-155	1951						
	G6HD-160	1951	PROOF					
	G6HD-165	1951	PROOF from sandblasted dies					
	G6HD-170	1952						
	G6HD-175	1952	PROOF					

Elizabeth II 1952 –

✓	No.	Date	Features	Grade	Purchased From	Date	Price Paid	Value Now
	EL2HD-005	1953						
	EL2HD-010	1953	PROOF					
	EL2HD-015	1953	PROOF from sandblasted dies					
	EL2HD-020	1954						
	EL2HD-025	1954	PROOF					
	EL2HD-030	1955						
	EL2HD-035	1955	PROOF					
	EL2HD-040	1956						
	EL2HD-045	1956	PROOF					
	EL2HD-050	1957						
	EL2HD-055	1957	PROOF					
	EL2HD-060	1958						
	EL2HD-065	1958	PROOF					
	EL2HD-070	1959						
	EL2HD-075	1959	PROOF					
	EL2HD-080	1960						
	EL2HD-085	1960	PROOF					
	EL2HD-090	1962						
	EL2HD-095	1962	PROOF					
	EL2HD-100	1963						
	EL2HD-105	1963	PROOF					
	EL2HD-110	1964						
	EL2HD-115	1964	PROOF					

Cont.

✓	No.	Date	Features	*Grade*	*Purchased From*	*Date*	*Price Paid*	*Value Now*
	EL2HD-120	1965						
	EL2HD-125	1965	PROOF					
	EL2HD-130	1965	struck in gold					
	EL2HD-135	1965	New Zealand halfpenny reverse					
	EL2HD-140	1966						
	EL2HD-145	1966	PROOF					
	EL2HD-150	1966	struck in aluminium					
	EL2HD-155	1966	struck in brass or nickel-brass					
	EL2HD-160	1967						
	EL2HD-165	1967	PROOF					
	EL2HD-170	1967	struck in cupronickel					
	EL2HD-175	1970	PROOF					

Farthing

George IV 1820 – 1830

✓	No.	Date	Features	*Grade*	*Purchased From*	*Date*	*Price Paid*	*Value Now*
	G4FA-005	1821						
	G4FA-010	1821	PROOF					
	G4FA-015	1822						
	G4FA-020	1822	PROOF; rev. ↓					
	G4FA-025	1823	1 in date is I					
	G4FA-030	1823	1 in date is 1					
	G4FA-035	1825						
	G4FA-040	1825	D of DEI over U (obv.)					
	G4FA-045	1825	PROOF in gold					
	G4FA-050	1826	obv. 1, rev. 1					
	G4FA-052	1826	R of GRATIA over E; obv. 1, rev. 1					
	G4FA-055	1826	obv. 2, rev. 2					
	G4FA-058	1826	Roman I in date; obv. 2, rev. 2					
	G4FA-060	1826	PROOF; obv. 2, rev. 2					
	G4FA-065	1826	Bronzed PROOF; obv. 2, rev. 2					
	G4FA-070	1827						
	G4FA-075	1828						
	G4FA-080	1829						
	G4FA-085	1830						

William IV 1830 – 1837

✓	No.	Date	Features	*Grade*	*Purchased From*	*Date*	*Price Paid*	*Value Now*
	W4FA-005	1831						
	W4FA-010	1831	PROOF					
	W4FA-015	1831	Bronzed PROOF					
	W4FA-020	1831	Bronzed PROOF rev. ↓					
	W4FA-025	1834						
	W4FA-030	1835						
	W4FA-035	1835	rev. ↓					
	W4FA-040	1836						
	W4FA-045	1837						
	W4FA-050	1837	7 over indeterminate digit					

Victoria 1837 – 1901

Copper Issue

✓	No.	Date	Features	*Grade*	*Purchased From*	*Date*	*Price Paid*	*Value Now*
	VYFA-005	1838						
	VYFA-010	1839						
	VYFA-015	1839	trident has only 2 prongs (rev.)					
	VYFA-020	1839	PROOF					
	VYFA-025	1839	Bronzed PROOF					

✓	No.	Date	Features	Grade	Purchased From	Date	Price Paid	Value Now
	VYFA-030	1839	Bronzed PROOF; rev. ↓					
	VYFA-035	1839	PROOF in silver					
	VYFA-040	1840						
	VYFA-042	1840	trident has only 2 prongs (rev.)					
	VYFA-045	1841						
	VYFA-050	1841	PROOF					
	VYFA-055	1842						
	VYFA-060	1843	1 in date is I					
	VYFA-065	1843	1 in date is 1					
	VYFA-068	1843	1 in date is 1; 3 over 2					
	VYFA-070	1844						
	VYFA-075	1845						
	VYFA-080	1846						
	VYFA-085	1847						
	VYFA-090	1848						
	VYFA-095	1849						
	VYFA-100	1850						
	VYFA-102	1850	5 over 7					
	VYFA-105	1851						
	VYFA-110	1851	D of DEI over horizontal D (obv.)					
	VYFA-115	1852						
	VYFA-120	1853	obv. 1					
	VYFA-125	1853	PROOF; obv. 1					
	VYFA-130	1853	Bronzed PROOF rev. ↓; obv. 1					
	VYFA-135	1853	obv. 2					
	VYFA-140	1853	PROOF; obv. 2					
	VYFA-145	1854						
	VYFA-150	1855	obv. 1					
	VYFA-155	1855	obv. 2					
	VYFA-160	1856						
	VYFA-165	1856	R of VICTORIA under E (obv.)					
	VYFA-170	1857						
	VYFA-175	1858						
	VYFA-178	1858	small date					
	VYFA-180	1859						
	VYFA-185	1860						

Bronze Issue; Young Head

✓	No.	Date	Features	Grade	Purchased From	Date	Price Paid	Value Now
	VYFA-190	1860	obv. 3, rev. 2					
	VYFA-195	1860	PROOF; obv. 3, rev. 2					
	VYFA-200	1860	obv. 4, rev. 2					
	VYFA-205	1860	obv. 4, rev. 3					
	VYFA-210	1860	PROOF; obv. 4, rev. 3					
	VYFA-215	1861						
	VYFA-220	1861	PROOF					
	VYFA-225	1861	PROOF in 0.97 silver					
	VYFA-230	1861	PROOF in gold; rev. ↓					
	VYFA-235	1862						
	VYFA-240	1862	PROOF					

Cont.

✓	No.	Date	Features	Grade	Purchased From	Date	Price Paid	Value Now
	VYFA-245	1863						
	VYFA-250	1863	PROOF					
	VYFA-255	1864	in copper; as copper issue					
	VYFA-260	1864						
	VYFA-265	1865						
	VYFA-270	1865	5 over 2					
	VYFA-275	1866						
	VYFA-280	1866	PROOF					
	VYFA-285	1867						
	VYFA-290	1867	PROOF					
	VYFA-295	1868						
	VYFA-300	1868	PROOF					
	VYFA-305	1868	PROOF in copper					
	VYFA-310	1868	PROOF in cupronickel					
	VYFA-315	1869						
	VYFA-320	1872						
	VYFA-325	1873						
	VYFA-330	1874	H below date					
	VYFA-335	1874	H below date; 'G's on obv. both over horizontal 'G's					
	VYFA-340	1874	H below date; PROOF					
	VYFA-345	1875	IWW on truncation					
	VYFA-350	1875	obv. 4					
	VYFA-355	1875	obv. 5					
	VYFA-360	1875	H below date; obv. 4					
	VYFA-365	1875	H below date; obv. 5					
	VYFA-370	1875	H below date; PROOF; obv. 5					
	VYFA-375	1876	H below date					
	VYFA-380	1877	PROOF					
	VYFA-385	1878						
	VYFA-390	1878	PROOF					
	VYFA-395	1879						
	VYFA-400	1879	PROOF					
	VYFA-405	1880						
	VYFA-410	1880	PROOF					
	VYFA-415	1881						
	VYFA-420	1881	PROOF					
	VYFA-425	1881	H below date					
	VYFA-430	1882	H below date					
	VYFA-435	1882	H below date; PROOF					
	VYFA-440	1883						
	VYFA-445	1883	PROOF					
	VYFA-450	1884						
	VYFA-455	1884	PROOF					
	VYFA-460	1885						
	VYFA-465	1885	PROOF					
	VYFA-470	1886						
	VYFA-475	1886	PROOF					
	VYFA-480	1887						
	VYFA-485	1888						
	VYFA-490	1890						
	VYFA-495	1890	PROOF					

Cont.

✓	No.	Date	Features	Grade	Purchased From	Date	Price Paid	Value Now
	VYFA-500	1891						
	VYFA-505	1891	PROOF					
	VYFA-510	1892						
	VYFA-515	1892	PROOF					
	VYFA-520	1893						
	VYFA-525	1894						
	VYFA-530	1894	PROOF					
	VYFA-535	1895						

Old Head

✓	No.	Date	Features	Grade	Purchased From	Date	Price Paid	Value Now
	VOFA-540	1895						
	VOFA-545	1895	PROOF					
	VOFA-550	1896						
	VOFA-555	1896	PROOF					
	VOFA-560	1897						
	VOFA-562	1897	issued artificially darkened					
	VOFA-565	1897	issued artificially darkened					
	VOFA-568	1897	issued with conventional bright finish					
	VOFA-570	1898	issued artificially darkened					
	VOFA-572	1898	issued with conventional bright finish					
	VOFA-575	1899	issued artificially darkened					
	VOFA-580	1900	issued artificially darkened					
	VOFA-585	1901	issued artificially darkened					
	VOFA-590	1901	issued with conventional bright finish					

Edward VII 1901 – 1910

✓	No.	Date	Features	Grade	Purchased From	Date	Price Paid	Value Now
	E7FA-005	1902						
	E7FA-010	1903						
	E7FA-015	1904						
	E7FA-020	1905						
	E7FA-025	1906						
	E7FA-030	1907						
	E7FA-035	1908						
	E7FA-040	1909						
	E7FA-045	1910						

George V 1910 – 1936

✓	No.	Date	Features	Grade	Purchased From	Date	Price Paid	Value Now
	G5FA-005	1911	issued artificially darkened					
	G5FA-010	1912	issued artificially darkened					
	G5FA-015	1913	issued artificially darkened					
	G5FA-020	1914	issued artificially darkened					
	G5FA-025	1915	issued artificially darkened					
	G5FA-030	1916	issued artificially darkened					
	G5FA-035	1917	issued artificially darkened					

Cont.

✓	No.	Date	Features	Grade	Purchased From	Date	Price Paid	Value Now
	G5FA-040	1918	some issued artificially darkened					
	G5FA-045	1919						
	G5FA-050	1920						
	G5FA-055	1921						
	G5FA-060	1922						
	G5FA-065	1923						
	G5FA-070	1924						
	G5FA-075	1925						
	G5FA-080	1926						
	G5FA-085	1926	PROOF					
	G5FA-090	1927						
	G5FA-095	1927	PROOF					
	G5FA-100	1928						
	G5FA-105	1928	PROOF					
	G5FA-110	1929						
	G5FA-115	1929	PROOF					
	G5FA-120	1930						
	G5FA-125	1930	PROOF					
	G5FA-130	1931						
	G5FA-135	1931	PROOF					
	G5FA-140	1932						
	G5FA-145	1932	PROOF					
	G5FA-150	1933						
	G5FA-155	1933	PROOF					
	G5FA-160	1934						
	G5FA-165	1934	PROOF					
	G5FA-170	1935						
	G5FA-175	1935	PROOF					
	G5FA-180	1936						
	G5FA-185	1936	PROOF					

Edward VIII 1936

✓	No.	Date	Features	Grade	Purchased From	Date	Price Paid	Value Now
	E8FA-005	1937						

George VI 1937 – 1952

✓	No.	Date	Features	Grade	Purchased From	Date	Price Paid	Value Now
	G6FA-005	1937						
	G6FA-010	1937	PROOF					
	G6FA-015	1937	PROOF from sandblasted dies					
	G6FA-020	1937	uniface rev. in silver					
	G6FA-025	1938						
	G6FA-030	1938	PROOF					
	G6FA-035	1939						
	G6FA-040	1939	PROOF					
	G6FA-045	1940						
	G6FA-050	1940	PROOF					
	G6FA-055	1941						

Cont.

✓	No.	Date	Features	Grade	Purchased From	Date	Price Paid	Value Now
	G6FA-060	1941	PROOF					
	G6FA-065	1942						
	G6FA-070	1942	PROOF					
	G6FA-075	1943						
	G6FA-080	1943	PROOF					
	G6FA-085	1944						
	G6FA-090	1944	PROOF					
	G6FA-095	1945						
	G6FA-100	1945	PROOF					
	G6FA-105	1946						
	G6FA-110	1946	PROOF					
	G6FA-115	1947						
	G6FA-120	1947	PROOF					
	G6FA-125	1948						
	G6FA-130	1948	PROOF					
	G6FA-135	1949						
	G6FA-140	1949	PROOF					
	G6FA-145	1950						
	G6FA-150	1950	PROOF					
	G6FA-155	1950	PROOF from sandblasted dies					
	G6FA-160	1951						
	G6FA-165	1951	PROOF					
	G6FA-170	1951	PROOF from sandblasted dies					
	G6FA-175	1951	in cupronickel					
	G6FA-180	1952						
	G6FA-185	1952	PROOF					

Elizabeth II 1952 –

✓	No.	Date	Features	Grade	Purchased From	Date	Price Paid	Value Now
	EL2FA-005	1953						
	EL2FA-010	1953	PROOF					
	EL2FA-015	1953	PROOF from sandblasted dies					
	EL2FA-020	1954						
	EL2FA-025	1954	PROOF					
	EL2FA-030	1955						
	EL2FA-035	1955	PROOF					
	EL2FA-040	1956						
	EL2FA-045	1956	PROOF					

Half Farthing

George IV 1820 – 1830

✓	No.	Date	Features	*Grade*	*Purchased From*	*Date*	*Price Paid*	*Value Now*
	G4HF-005	1828						
	G4HF-010	1828	PROOF					
	G4HF-015	1828	Bronzed PROOF rev. ↓					
	G4HF-020	1830						
	G4HF-025	1830	PROOF					

William IV 1830 – 1837

✓	No.	Date	Features	*Grade*	*Purchased From*	*Date*	*Price Paid*	*Value Now*
	W4HF-005	1837						

Victoria 1837 – 1901

✓	No.	Date	Features	*Grade*	*Purchased From*	*Date*	*Price Paid*	*Value Now*
	VYHF-005	1839						
	VYHF-010	1839	Bronzed PROOF					
	VYHF-015	1842						
	VYHF-020	1843						
	VYHF-025	1844						
	VYHF-030	1844	E of REGINA over N (obv.)					
	VYHF-035	1847						
	VYHF-040	1851						
	VYHF-045	1851	first 1 over 5					
	VYHF-050	1852						
	VYHF-055	1853						
	VYHF-060	1853	PROOF					
	VYHF-065	1853	Bronzed PROOF; rev. ↓					
	VYHF-070	1854						
	VYHF-075	1856						
	VYHF-080	1868	PROOF in bronze					
	VYHF-085	1868	PROOF in cupronickel					

Third Farthing

George IV 1820 – 1830

✓	No.	Date	Features	Grade	Purchased From	Date	Price Paid	Value Now
	G4TF-005	1827						
	G4TF-010	1827	PROOF					

William IV 1830 – 1837

✓	No.	Date	Features	Grade	Purchased From	Date	Price Paid	Value Now
	W4TF-005	1835						
	W4TF-010	1835	PROOF					

Victoria 1837 – 1901

✓	No.	Date	Features	Grade	Purchased From	Date	Price Paid	Value Now
	VYTF-005	1844						
	VYTF-010	1844	large G in REG (obv.)					
	VYTF-015	1844	RE instead of REG (obv.)					
	VYTF-020	1866						
	VYTF-025	1866	PROOF					
	VYTF-030	1868						
	VYTF-035	1868	PROOF					
	VYTF-040	1868	PROOF in cupronickel					
	VYTF-045	1868	PROOF in aluminium					
	VYTF-050	1876						
	VYTF-055	1878						
	VYTF-060	1881						
	VYTF-065	1881	PROOF					
	VYTF-070	1884						
	VYTF-075	1885						

Edward VII 1901 – 1910

✓	No.	Date	Features	Grade	Purchased From	Date	Price Paid	Value Now
	E7TF-005	1902						

George V 1910 – 1936

✓	No.	Date	Features	Grade	Purchased From	Date	Price Paid	Value Now
	G5TF-005	1913						

Quarter Farthing

Victoria 1837 – 1901

✓	No.	Date	Features	*Grade*	*Purchased From*	*Date*	*Price Paid*	*Value Now*
	VYQF-005	1839						
	VYQF-010	1851						
	VYQF-015	1852						
	VYQF-020	1852	Bronzed PROOF					
	VYQF-025	1853						
	VYQF-030	1853	PROOF					
	VYQF-035	1853	Bronzed PROOF					
	VYQF-040	1868	PROOF					
	VYQF-045	1868	PROOF in cupronickel					

Maundy Sets

George IV 1820 – 1830

✓	No.	Date	Features	*Grade*	*Purchased From*	*Date*	*Price Paid*	*Value Now*
	G4MS-005	1822						
	G4MS-010	1822	PROOFS					
	G4MS-015	1823						
	G4MS-020	1824						
	G4MS-025	1825						
	G4MS-030	1826						
	G4MS-035	1827						
	G4MS-040	1828						
	G4MS-045	1828	PROOFS					
	G4MS-050	1829						
	G4MS-055	1830						

William IV 1830 – 1837

✓	No.	Date	Features	*Grade*	*Purchased From*	*Date*	*Price Paid*	*Value Now*
	W4MS-005	1831						
	W4MS-010	1831	PROOFS					
	W4MS-015	1831	PROOFS in gold					
	W4MS-020	1832						
	W4MS-025	1833						
	W4MS-030	1834						
	W4MS-035	1835						
	W4MS-040	1836						
	W4MS-045	1837						

Victoria 1837 – 1901

Young Head

✓	No.	Date	Features	*Grade*	*Purchased From*	*Date*	*Price Paid*	*Value Now*
	VYMS-005	1838						
	VYMS-010	1838	PROOFS					
	VYMS-015	1838	PROOFS in gold; revs ↓					
	VYMS-020	1839						
	VYMS-025	1839	PROOFS; revs ↓					
	VYMS-030	1840						
	VYMS-035	1841						
	VYMS-040	1842						
	VYMS-045	1843						
	VYMS-050	1844						
	VYMS-055	1845						
	VYMS-060	1846						
	VYMS-065	1847						
	VYMS-070	1848						

✓	No.	Date	Features	*Grade*	*Purchased From*	*Date*	*Price Paid*	*Value Now*
	VYMS-075	1849						
	VYMS-080	1850						
	VYMS-085	1851						
	VYMS-090	1852						
	VYMS-095	1853						
	VYMS-100	1853	PROOFS					
	VYMS-105	1854						
	VYMS-110	1855						
	VYMS-115	1856						
	VYMS-120	1857						
	VYMS-125	1857	2 pence reads BRITANNIAE EEGINA (obv.)					
	VYMS-130	1858						
	VYMS-135	1859						
	VYMS-140	1859	2 pence reads BEITANNIAR (rev.)					
	VYMS-145	1860						
	VYMS-150	1861	2 pence has 6 not over 1					
	VYMS-155	1861	2 pence has 6 over 1					
	VYMS-160	1862						
	VYMS-165	1863						
	VYMS-170	1864						
	VYMS-175	1865						
	VYMS-180	1866						
	VYMS-185	1867						
	VYMS-190	1867	PROOFS					
	VYMS-195	1868						
	VYMS-200	1869						
	VYMS-205	1870						
	VYMS-210	1871						
	VYMS-215	1871	PROOFS; revs ↓					
	VYMS-220	1872						
	VYMS-225	1873						
	VYMS-230	1874						
	VYMS-235	1875						
	VYMS-240	1876						
	VYMS-245	1877						
	VYMS-250	1878						
	VYMS-255	1878	PROOFS					
	VYMS-260	1879						
	VYMS-265	1879	PROOFS; revs ↓					
	VYMS-270	1880						
	VYMS-275	1881						
	VYMS-280	1881	PROOFS					
	VYMS-285	1882						
	VYMS-290	1883						
	VYMS-295	1884						
	VYMS-300	1885						
	VYMS-305	1886						
	VYMS-310	1887						

Jubilee Head

✓	No.	Date	Features	Grade	Purchased From	Date	Price Paid	Value Now
	VJMS-315	1888						
	VJMS-320	1888	PROOFS					
	VJMS-325	1889						
	VJMS-330	1890						
	VJMS-335	1891						
	VJMS-340	1892						

Old Head

✓	No.	Date	Features	Grade	Purchased From	Date	Price Paid	Value Now
	VOMS-345	1893						
	VOMS-350	1894						
	VOMS-355	1895						
	VOMS-360	1896						
	VOMS-365	1897						
	VOMS-370	1898						
	VOMS-375	1899						
	VOMS-380	1900						
	VOMS-385	1901						

Edward VII 1901 – 1910

✓	No.	Date	Features	Grade	Purchased From	Date	Price Paid	Value Now
	E7MS-005	1902						
	E7MS-010	1902	PROOFS					
	E7MS-015	1903						
	E7MS-020	1904						
	E7MS-025	1905						
	E7MS-030	1906						
	E7MS-035	1907						
	E7MS-040	1908						
	E7MS-045	1909						
	E7MS-050	1910						

George V 1910 – 1936

Sterling Silver Issue

✓	No.	Date	Features	Grade	Purchased From	Date	Price Paid	Value Now
	G5MS-005	1911						
	G5MS-010	1912						
	G5MS-015	1913						
	G5MS-020	1914						
	G5MS-025	1915						
	G5MS-030	1916						
	G5MS-035	1917						
	G5MS-040	1918						
	G5MS-045	1919						
	G5MS-050	1920						

50% Silver Issue

✓	No.	Date	Features	Grade	Purchased From	Date	Price Paid	Value Now
	G5MS-055	1921						
	G5MS-060	1922						
	G5MS-065	1923						
	G5MS-070	1924						
	G5MS-075	1925						
	G5MS-080	1926						
	G5MS-085	1927						
	G5MS-090	1928						
	G5MS-095	1929						
	G5MS-100	1930						
	G5MS-105	1931						
	G5MS-110	1932						
	G5MS-115	1933						
	G5MS-120	1934						
	G5MS-125	1935						
	G5MS-130	1936						

George VI 1937 – 1952

50% Silver Issue

✓	No.	Date	Features	Grade	Purchased From	Date	Price Paid	Value Now
	G6MS-005	1937						
	G6MS-010	1937	PROOF from sandblasted dies					
	G6MS-015	1938						
	G6MS-020	1939						
	G6MS-025	1940						
	G6MS-030	1941						
	G6MS-035	1942						
	G6MS-040	1943						
	G6MS-045	1944						
	G6MS-050	1945						
	G6MS-055	1946						

Sterling Silver Issue

✓	No.	Date	Features	Grade	Purchased From	Date	Price Paid	Value Now
	G6MS-060	1947						
	G6MS-065	1948						
	G6MS-070	1949						
	G6MS-075	1950						
	G6MS-080	1951						
	G6MS-085	1951	PROOF from sandblasted dies					
	G6MS-090	1952						
	G6MS-095	1952	struck in copper					

Elizabeth II 1952 –

✓	No.	Date	Features	*Grade*	*Purchased From*	*Date*	*Price Paid*	*Value Now*
	EL2MS-005	1953						
	EL2MS-010	1953	PROOF from sandblasted dies					
	EL2MS-015	1953	struck in gold					
	EL2MS-020	1954						
	EL2MS-025	1955						
	EL2MS-030	1956						
	EL2MS-035	1957						
	EL2MS-040	1958						
	EL2MS-045	1959						
	EL2MS-050	1960						
	EL2MS-055	1961						
	EL2MS-060	1962						
	EL2MS-065	1963						
	EL2MS-070	1964						
	EL2MS-075	1965						
	EL2MS-080	1966						
	EL2MS-085	1967						
	EL2MS-090	1968						
	EL2MS-095	1969						
	EL2MS-100	1970						
	EL2MS-105	1971						
	EL2MS-110	1972						
	EL2MS-115	1973						
	EL2MS-120	1974						
	EL2MS-125	1975						
	EL2MS-130	1976						
	EL2MS-135	1977						
	EL2MS-140	1978						
	EL2MS-145	1979						
	EL2MS-150	1980						
	EL2MS-155	1981						
	EL2MS-160	1982						
	EL2MS-165	1983						
	EL2MS-170	1984						
	EL2MS-175	1985						
	EL2MS-180	1986						
	EL2MS-185	1987						
	EL2MS-190	1988						
	EL2MS-195	1989						
	EL2MS-200	1990						
	EL2MS-205	1991						
	EL2MS-210	1992						
	EL2MS-215	1993						
	EL2MS-220	1994						
	EL2MS-225	1995						
	EL2MS-230	1996						
	EL2MS-235	1997						

Decimal Coinage Primarily Struck In Base Metals

Base Metal Five Pounds

✓	No.	Date	Features	*Grade*	*Purchased From*	*Date*	*Price Paid*	*Value Now*
	D5P/90-1	1990						
	D5P/90-2	1990	SPECIMEN					
	D5P/90-4	1990	PROOF in silver					
	D5P/90-6	1990	PROOF in gold					
	D5P/93-1	1993						
	D5P/93-2	1993	SPECIMEN					
	D5P/93-3	1993	PROOF					
	D5P/93-4	1993	PROOF in silver					
	D5P/93-6	1993	PROOF in gold					
	D5P/96-1	1996						
	D5P/96-2	1996	SPECIMEN					
	D5P/96-3	1996	PROOF					
	D5P/96-4	1996	PROOF in silver					
	D5P/96-6	1996	PROOF in gold					
	D5P/97-1	1997						
	D5P/97-2	1997	SPECIMEN					
	D5P/97-3	1997	PROOF					
	D5P/97-4	1997	PROOF in silver					
	D5P/97-6	1997	PROOF in gold					

Base Metal Two Pounds

✓	No.	Date	Features	*Grade*	*Purchased From*	*Date*	*Price Paid*	*Value Now*
	D2P/86-1	1986						
	D2P/86-2	1986	SPECIMEN					
	D2P/86-3	1986	PROOF					
	D2P/86SP-4	1986	SPECIMEN in 0.500 silver					
	D2P/86-4	1986	PROOF in silver					
	EL22P-030	1986	PROOF in gold					
	D2P/89CB-1	1989	rev. 2					
	D2P/89CB-2	1989	SPECIMEN; rev. 2					
	D2P/89CB-3	1989	PROOF; rev. 2					
	D2P/89CB-4	1989	PROOF in silver; rev. 2					
	D2P/89CB-5	1989	PIEDFORT PROOF in silver; rev. 2					
	D2P/89CC-1	1989	rev. 3					
	D2P/89CC-2	1989	SPECIMEN; rev. 3					
	D2P/89CC-3	1989	PROOF; rev. 3					
	D2P/89CC-4	1989	PROOF in silver; rev. 3					
	D2P/89CC-5	1989	PIEDFORT PROOF in silver; rev. 3					
	D2P/94-1	1994						
	D2P/94-2	1994	SPECIMEN					
	D2P/94-3	1994	PROOF					
	D2P/94-4	1994	PROOF in silver					

✓	No.	Date	Features	Grade	Purchased From	Date	Price Paid	Value Now
	D2P/94–5	1994	PIEDFORT PROOF in silver					
	EL22P-070	1994	PROOF in gold					
	EL22P-075	1994	PROOF in gold; error obv. 2					
	D2P/95C1–1	1995	rev. 5					
	D2P/95C1–2	1995	SPECIMEN; rev. 5					
	D2P/95C1–3	1995	PROOF; rev. 5					
	D2P/95C1–4	1995	PROOF in silver; rev. 5					
	D2P/95C1–5	1995	PIEDFORT PROOF in silver; rev. 5					
	EL22P-080	1995	PROOF in gold; rev. 5					
	D2P/95C2–1	1995	rev. 6					
	D2P/95C2–2	1995	SPECIMEN; rev. 6					
	D2P/95C2–3	1995	PROOF; rev. 6					
	D2P/95C2–4	1995	PROOF in silver; rev. 6					
	D2P/95C2–5	1995	PIEDFORT PROOF in silver; rev. 6					
	EL22P-085	1995	PROOF in gold; rev. 6					
	D2P/96–1	1996						
	D2P/96–2	1996	SPECIMEN					
	D2P/96–3	1996	PROOF					
	D2P/96–4	1996	PROOF in silver					
	D2P/96–6	1996	PROOF in gold					
	D2P/97–1	1997						
	D2P/97–2	1997	SPECIMEN					
	D2P/97–3	1997	PROOF					
	D2P/97–4	1997	PROOF in silver					
	D2P/97–5	1997	PIEDFORT PROOF in silver					
	EL22P-095	1997	PIEDFORT PROOF in gold					

Base Metal One Pound

✓	No.	Date	Features	Grade	Purchased From	Date	Price Paid	Value Now
	D1P/83–1	1983						
	D1P/83–2	1983	SPECIMEN					
	D1P/83–3	1983	PROOF					
	D1P/83–4	1983	PROOF in silver					
	D1P/83–5	1983	PIEDFORT PROOF in silver					
	D1P/84–1	1984						
	D1P/84–2	1984	SPECIMEN					
	D1P/84–3	1984	PROOF					
	D1P/84–4	1984	PROOF in silver					
	D1P/84–5	1984	PIEDFORT PROOF in silver					
	D1P/85–1	1985						
	D1P/85–2	1985	SPECIMEN					
	D1P/85–3	1985	PROOF					
	D1P/85–4	1985	PROOF in silver					
	D1P/85–5	1985	PIEDFORT PROOF in silver					
	D1P/86–1	1986						
	D1P/86–2	1986	SPECIMEN					
	D1P/86–3	1986	PROOF					
	D1P/86–4	1986	PROOF in silver					
	D1P/86–5	1986	PIEDFORT PROOF in silver					

Cont.

✓	No.	Date	Features	*Grade*	*Purchased From*	*Date*	*Price Paid*	*Value Now*
	D1P/87–1	1987						
	D1P/87–2	1987	SPECIMEN					
	D1P/87–3	1987	PROOF					
	D1P/87–4	1987	PROOF in silver					
	D1P/87–5	1987	PIEDFORT PROOF in silver					
	D1P/88–1	1988						
	D1P/88–2	1988	SPECIMEN					
	D1P/88–3	1988	PROOF					
	D1P/88–4	1988	PROOF in silver					
	D1P/88–5	1988	PIEDFORT PROOF in silver					
	D1P/89–1	1989						
	D1P/89–2	1989	SPECIMEN					
	D1P/89–3	1989	PROOF					
	D1P/89–4	1989	PROOF in silver					
	D1P/89–5	1989	PIEDFORT PROOF in silver					
	D1P/90–1	1990						
	D1P/90–3	1990	PROOF					
	D1P/90–4	1990	PROOF in silver					
	D1P/91–1	1991						
	D1P/91–3	1991	PROOF					
	D1P/91–4	1991	PROOF in silver					
	D1P/92–1	1992						
	D1P/92–3	1992	PROOF					
	D1P/92–4	1992	PROOF in silver					
	D1P/93–1	1993						
	D1P/93–3	1993	PROOF					
	D1P/93–4	1993	PROOF in silver					
	D1P/93–5	1993	PIEDFORT PROOF in silver					
	D1P/94–1	1994						
	D1P/94–2	1994	SPECIMEN					
	D1P/94–3	1994	PROOF					
	D1P/94–4	1994	PROOF in silver					
	D1P/94–5	1994	PIEDFORT PROOF in silver					
	D1P/95–1	1995						
	D1P/95–3	1995	PROOF					
	D1P/95–4	1995	PROOF in silver					
	D1P/95–5	1995	PIEDFORT PROOF in silver					
	D1P/96–1	1996						
	D1P/96–2	1996	SPECIMEN					
	D1P/96–3	1996	PROOF					
	D1P/96–4	1996	PROOF in silver					
	D1P/96–5	1996	PIEDFORT PROOF in silver					
	D1P/97–1	1997						
	D1P/97–2	1997	SPECIMEN					
	D1P/97–3	1997	PROOF					
	D1P/97–4	1997	PROOF in silver					
	D1P/97–5	1997	PIEDFORT PROOF in silver					

50 Pence

30 mm diameter

✓	No.	Date	Features	*Grade*	*Purchased From*	*Date*	*Price Paid*	*Value Now*
	D50/69–1	1969						
	D50/69–1E	1969						
	D50/70–1	1970						
	D50/71–3	1971	PROOF					
	D50/72–3	1972	PROOF					
	D50/73–1	1973						
	D50/73–3	1973	PROOF					
	D50/73–5	1973	PIEDFORT PROOF in silver					
	D50/74–3	1974	PROOF					
	D50/75–3	1975	PROOF					
	D50/76–1	1976						
	D50/76–3	1976	PROOF					
	D50/77–1	1977						
	D50/77–3	1977	PROOF					
	D50/78–1	1978						
	D50/78–3	1978	PROOF					
	D50/79–1	1979						
	D50/79–3	1979	PROOF					
	D50/80–1	1980						
	D50/80–3	1980	PROOF					
	D50/81–1	1981						
	D50/81–3	1981	PROOF					
	D50/RR-1E		rev. 1 on both sides (no date)					
	D50/82–1	1982						
	D50/82–3	1982	PROOF					
	D50/83–1	1983						
	D50/83–3	1983	PROOF					
	D50/84–1	1984						
	D50/84–3	1984	PROOF					
	D50/85–1	1985						
	D50/85–3	1985	PROOF					
	D50/86–1	1986						
	D50/86–3	1986	PROOF					
	D50/87–1	1987						
	D50/87–3	1987	PROOF					
	D50/88–1	1988						
	D50/88–3	1988	PROOF					
	D50/89–1	1989						
	D50/89–3	1989	PROOF					
	D50/90–1	1990						
	D50/90–3	1990	PROOF					
	D50/91–1	1991						
	D50/91–3	1991	PROOF					
	D50/92–1	1992						
	D50/92–3	1992	PROOF					
	D50/93–1	1993						
	D50/93–3	1993	PROOF					

Cont.

✓	No.	Date	Features	Grade	Purchased From	Date	Price Paid	Value Now
	D50/92C-1	1992/93						
	D50/92C-3	1992/93	PROOF					
	D50/92C-4	1992/93	PROOF in silver					
	D50/92C-5	1992/93	PIEDFORT PROOF in silver					
	D50/92C-6	1992/93	PROOF in gold					
	D50/94C-1	1994						
	D50/94C-2	1994	SPECIMEN					
	D50/94C-3	1994	PROOF					
	D50/94C-4	1994	PROOF in silver					
	D50/94C-5	1994	PIEDFORT PROOF in silver					
	D50/94C-6	1994	PROOF in gold					
	D50/95–1	1995						
	D50/95–3	1995	PROOF					
	D50/96–1	1996						
	D50/96–3	1996	PROOF					
	D50/96–4	1996	PROOF in silver					
	D50/97–3L	1997	PROOF					

27 mm diameter

✓	No.	Date	Features	Grade	Purchased From	Date	Price Paid	Value Now
	D50/97–1	1997						
	D50/97–3S	1997	PROOF					

25 Pence

✓	No.	Date	Features	Grade	Purchased From	Date	Price Paid	Value Now
	D25/72–1	1972						
	D25/72–3	1972	PROOF					
	D25/72–4	1972	PROOF in silver					
	D25/77–1	1977						
	D25/77–2	1977	SPECIMEN					
	D25/77–3	1977	PROOF					
	D25/77–4	1977	PROOF in silver					
	D25/80–1	1980						
	D25/80–2	1980	SPECIMEN					
	D25/80–4	1980	PROOF in silver					
	D25/81–1	1981						
	D25/81–2	1981	SPECIMEN					
	D25/81–4	1981	PROOF in silver					

20 Pence

✓	No.	Date	Features	Grade	Purchased From	Date	Price Paid	Value Now
	D20/82–1	1982						
	D20/82–3	1982	PROOF					
	D20/82–5	1982	PIEDFORT PROOF in silver					
	D20/83–1	1983						
	D20/83–3	1983	PROOF					
	D20/84–1	1984						

Cont.

✓	No.	Date	Features	*Grade*	*Purchased From*	*Date*	*Price Paid*	*Value Now*
	D20/84–3	1984	PROOF					
	D20/85–1	1985						
	D20/85–3	1985	PROOF					
	D20/86–1	1986						
	D20/86–3	1986	PROOF					
	D20/87–1	1987						
	D20/87–3	1987	PROOF					
	D20/88–1	1988						
	D20/88–3	1988	PROOF					
	D20/89–1	1989						
	D20/89–3	1989	PROOF					
	D20/90–1	1990						
	D20/90–3	1990	PROOF					
	D20/91–1	1991						
	D20/91–3	1991	PROOF					
	D20/92–1	1992						
	D20/92–3	1992	PROOF					
	D20/93–1	1993						
	D20/93–3	1993	PROOF					
	D20/94–1	1994						
	D20/94–3	1994	PROOF					
	D20/95–1	1995						
	D20/95–3	1995	PROOF					
	D20/96–1	1996						
	D20/96–3	1996	PROOF					
	D20/96–4	1996	PROOF in silver					
	D20/97–1	1997						
	D20/97–3	1997	PROOF					

10 Pence

28.5 mm diameter

✓	No.	Date	Features	*Grade*	*Purchased From*	*Date*	*Price Paid*	*Value Now*
	D10/68–1	1968						
	D10/69–1	1969						
	D10/70–1	1970						
	D10/71–1	1971						
	D10/71–3	1971	PROOF					
	D10/72–3	1972	PROOF					
	D10/73–1	1973						
	D10/73–3	1973	PROOF					
	D10/74–1	1974						
	D10/74–1E	1974	struck on thin flan					
	D10/74–3	1974	PROOF					
	D10/75–1	1975						
	D10/75–3	1975	PROOF					
	D10/76–1	1976						
	D10/76–3	1976	PROOF					
	D10/77–1	1977						
	D10/77–3	1977	PROOF					

Cont.

✓	No.	Date	Features	Grade	Purchased From	Date	Price Paid	Value Now
	D10/78–3	1978	PROOF					
	D10/79–1	1979						
	D10/79–3	1979	PROOF					
	D10/80–1	1980						
	D10/80–3	1980	PROOF					
	D10/81–1	1981						
	D10/81–3	1981	PROOF					
	D10/82–1	1982						
	D10/82–3	1982	PROOF					
	D10/83–1	1983						
	D10/83–3	1983	PROOF					
	D10/84–1	1984						
	D10/84–3	1984	PROOF					
	D10/85–1	1985						
	D10/85–3	1985	PROOF					
	D10/86–1	1986						
	D10/86–3	1986	PROOF					
	D10/87–1	1987						
	D10/87–3	1987	PROOF					
	D10/88–1	1988						
	D10/88–3	1988	PROOF					
	D10/89–1	1989						
	D10/89–3	1989	PROOF					
	D10/90–1	1990						
	D10/90–3	1990	PROOF					
	D10/91–1	1991						
	D10/91–3	1991	PROOF					
	D10/92–1L	1992						
	D10/92–3L	1992	PROOF					
	D10/92–4L	1992	PROOF in silver					

24.5 mm diameter

✓	No.	Date	Features	Grade	Purchased From	Date	Price Paid	Value Now
	D10/92–1S	1992						
	D10/92–3S	1992	PROOF					
	D10/92–4S	1992	PROOF in silver					
	D10/92–5S	1992	PIEDFORT PROOF in silver					
	D10/93–1	1993						
	D10/93–3	1993	PROOF					
	D10/94–1	1994						
	D10/94–3	1994	PROOF					
	D10/95–1	1995						
	D10/95–3	1995	PROOF					
	D10/96–1	1996						
	D10/96–3	1996	PROOF					
	D10/96–4	1996	PROOF in silver					
	D10/97–1	1997						
	D10/97–3	1997	PROOF					

5 Pence

24 mm diameter

✓	No.	Date	Features	Grade	Purchased From	Date	Price Paid	Value Now
	D05/68–1	1968						
	D05/69–1	1969						
	D05/70–1	1970						
	D05/71–1	1971						
	D05/71–3	1971	PROOF					
	D05/72–3	1972	PROOF					
	D05/73–3	1973	PROOF					
	D05/74–3	1974	PROOF					
	D05/75–1	1975						
	D05/75–3	1975	PROOF					
	D05/76–3	1976	PROOF					
	D05/77–1	1977						
	D05/77–3	1977	PROOF					
	D05/78–1	1978						
	D05/78–3	1978	PROOF					
	D05/79–1	1979						
	D05/79–3	1979	PROOF					
	D05/80–1	1980						
	D05/80–3	1980	PROOF					
	D05/81–3	1981	PROOF					
	D05/82–1	1982						
	D05/82–3	1982	PROOF					
	D05/83–1	1983						
	D05/83–3	1983	PROOF					
	D05/84–1	1984						
	D05/84–3	1984	PROOF					
	D05/85–1	1985						
	D05/85–3	1985	PROOF					
	D05/86–1	1986						
	D05/86–3	1986	PROOF					
	D05/87–1	1987						
	D05/87–3	1987	PROOF					
	D05/88–1	1988						
	D05/88–3	1988	PROOF					
	D05/89–1	1989						
	D05/89–3	1989	PROOF					
	D05/90–1L	1990						
	D05/90–3L	1990	PROOF					
	D05/90–4L	1990	PROOF in silver					

18 mm diameter

✓	No.	Date	Features	Grade	Purchased From	Date	Price Paid	Value Now
	D05/90–1S	1990						
	D05/90–3S	1990	PROOF					
	D05/90–4S	1990	PROOF in silver					
	D05/90–5S	1990	PIEDFORT PROOF in silver					

Cont.

✓	No.	Date	Features	Grade	Purchased From	Date	Price Paid	Value Now
	D05/91–1	1991						
	D05/91–3	1991	PROOF					
	D05/92–1	1992						
	D05/92–3	1992	PROOF					
	D05/93–1	1993						
	D05/93–3	1993	PROOF					
	D05/94–1	1994						
	D05/94–3	1994	PROOF					
	D05/95–1	1995						
	D05/95–3	1995	PROOF					
	D05/96–1	1996						
	D05/96–3	1996	PROOF					
	D05/96–4	1996	PROOF in silver					
	D05/97–1	1997						
	D05/97–3	1997	PROOF					

2 Pence

Bronze Issue

✓	No.	Date	Features	Grade	Purchased From	Date	Price Paid	Value Now
	D02/71–1	1971						
	D02/71–3	1971	PROOF					
	D02/72–3	1972	PROOF					
	D02/73–3	1973	PROOF					
	D02/74–3	1974	PROOF					
	D02/75–1	1975						
	D02/75–3	1975	PROOF					
	D02/76–1	1976						
	D02/76–3	1976	PROOF					
	D02/77–1	1977						
	D02/77–3	1977	PROOF					
	D02/78–1	1978						
	D02/78–3	1978	PROOF					
	D02/79–1	1979						
	D02/79–3	1979	PROOF					
	D02/80–1	1980						
	D02/80–3	1980	PROOF					
	D02/81–1	1981						
	D02/81–3	1981	PROOF					
	D02/RR-1		Rev. 1 both sides (no date)					
	D02/82–1	1982						
	D02/82–3	1982	PROOF					
	D02/83–1E	1983	error reverse					
	D02/83–1	1983						
	D02/83–3	1983	PROOF					
	D02/84–1	1984						
	D02/84–3	1984	PROOF					
	D02/85–1	1985						
	D02/85–3	1985	PROOF					
	D02/86–1	1986						

Cont.

✓	No.	Date	Features	Grade	Purchased From	Date	Price Paid	Value Now
	D02/86-3	1986	PROOF					
	D02/87-1	1987						
	D02/87-3	1987	PROOF					
	D02/88-1	1988						
	D02/88-3	1988	PROOF					
	D02/89-1	1989						
	D02/89-3	1989	PROOF					
	D02/90-1	1990						
	D02/90-3	1990	PROOF					
	D02/91-1	1991						
	D02/91-3	1991	PROOF					
	D02/92-1BR	1992	bronze issue					
	D02/92-3	1992	bronze issue PROOF					

Copper Plated Steel Issue

✓	No.	Date	Features	Grade	Purchased From	Date	Price Paid	Value Now
	D02/92-1ST	1992	copper plated steel issue					
	D02/93-1	1993						
	D02/93-3	1993	PROOF					
	D02/94-1	1994						
	D02/94-3	1994	PROOF					
	D02/95-1	1995						
	D02/95-3	1995	PROOF					
	D02/96-1	1996						
	D02/96-3	1996	PROOF					
	D02/96-4	1996	PROOF in silver					
	D02/97-1	1997						
	D02/97-3	1997	PROOF					

1 Penny

Bronze Issue

✓	No.	Date	Features	Grade	Purchased From	Date	Price Paid	Value Now
	D01/71-1	1971						
	D01/71-3	1971	PROOF					
	D01/72-3	1972	PROOF					
	D01/73-1	1973						
	D01/73-3	1973	PROOF					
	D01/74-1	1974						
	D01/74-3	1974	PROOF					
	D01/75-1	1975						
	D01/75-3	1975	PROOF					
	D01/76-1	1976						
	D01/76-3	1976	PROOF					
	D01/77-1	1977						
	D01/77-3	1977	PROOF					
	D01/78-1	1978						
	D01/78-3	1978	PROOF					
	D01/79-1	1979						

Cont.

✓	No.	Date	Features	Grade	Purchased From	Date	Price Paid	Value Now
	D01/79–3	1979	PROOF					
	D01/80–1	1980						
	D01/80–3	1980	PROOF					
	D01/81–1	1981						
	D01/81–3	1981	PROOF					
	D01/82–1	1982						
	D01/82–3	1982	PROOF					
	D01/83–1	1983						
	D01/83–3	1983	PROOF					
	D01/84–1	1984						
	D01/84–3	1984	PROOF					
	D01/85–1	1985						
	D01/85–3	1985	PROOF					
	D01/86–1	1986						
	D01/86–3	1986	PROOF					
	D01/87–1	1987						
	D01/87–3	1987	PROOF					
	D01/88–1	1988						
	D01/88–3	1988	PROOF					
	D01/89–1	1989						
	D01/89–3	1989	PROOF					
	D01/90–1	1990						
	D01/90–3	1990	PROOF					
	D01/91–1	1991						
	D01/91–3	1991	PROOF					
	D01/92–1BR	1992						
	D01/92–3	1992	PROOF					

Copper Plated Steel Issue

✓	No.	Date	Features	Grade	Purchased From	Date	Price Paid	Value Now
	D01/92–1ST	1992						
	D01/93–1	1993						
	D01/93–3	1993	PROOF					
	D01/94–1	1994						
	D01/94–3	1994	PROOF					
	D01/95–1	1995						
	D01/95–3	1995	PROOF					
	D01/96–1	1996						
	D01/96–3	1996	PROOF					
	D01/96–4	1996	PROOF in silver					
	D01/97–1	1997						
	D01/97–3	1997	PROOF					

Half Penny

✓	No.	Date	Features	Grade	Purchased From	Date	Price Paid	Value Now
	DHP/71–1	1971						
	DHP/71–1E	1971						
	DHP/71–3	1971	PROOF					
	DHP/72–3	1972	PROOF					

Cont.

✓	No.	Date	Features	*Grade*	*Purchased From*	*Date*	*Price Paid*	*Value Now*
	DHP/73–1	1973						
	DHP/73–3	1973	PROOF					
	DHP/74–1	1974						
	DHP/74–3	1974	PROOF					
	DHP/75–1	1975						
	DHP/75–3	1975	PROOF					
	DHP/76–1	1976						
	DHP/76–3	1976	PROOF					
	DHP/77–1	1977						
	DHP/77–3	1977	PROOF					
	DHP/78–1	1978						
	DHP/78–3	1978	PROOF					
	DHP/79–1	1979						
	DHP/79–3	1979	PROOF					
	DHP/80–1	1980						
	DHP/80–3	1980	PROOF					
	DHP/81–1	1981						
	DHP/81–3	1981	PROOF					
	DHP/82–1	1982						
	DHP/82–3	1982	PROOF					
	DHP/83–1	1983						
	DHP/83–3	1983	PROOF					
	DHP/84–1	1984						
	DHP/84–3	1984	PROOF					

Britannia Gold Coinage

100 Pounds

✓	No.	Date	Features	*Grade*	*Purchased From*	*Date*	*Price Paid*	*Value Now*
	BR100–005	1987						
	BR100–010	1987	PROOF					
	BR100–015	1988						
	BR100–020	1988	PROOF					
	BR100–025	1989						
	BR100–030	1989	PROOF					
	BR100–035	1990						
	BR100–040	1990	PROOF					
	BR100–045	1991						
	BR100–050	1991	PROOF					
	BR100–055	1992						
	BR100–060	1992	PROOF					
	BR100–065	1993						
	BR100–070	1993	PROOF					
	BR100–075	1994						
	BR100–080	1994	PROOF					
	BR100–085	1995						
	BR100–090	1995	PROOF					
	BR100–095	1996						
	BR100–100	1996	PROOF					
	BR100–105	1997						
	BR100–110	1997	PROOF					

50 Pounds

✓	No.	Date	Features	*Grade*	*Purchased From*	*Date*	*Price Paid*	*Value Now*
	BR50–005	1987						
	BR50–010	1987	PROOF					
	BR50–015	1988						
	BR50–020	1988	PROOF					
	BR50–025	1989						
	BR50–030	1989	PROOF					
	BR50–035	1990						
	BR50–040	1990	PROOF					
	BR50–045	1991						
	BR50–050	1991	PROOF					
	BR50–055	1992						
	BR50–060	1992	PROOF					
	BR50–065	1993						
	BR50–070	1993	PROOF					
	BR50–075	1994						
	BR50–080	1994	PROOF					
	BR50–085	1995						
	BR50–090	1995	PROOF					

✓	No.	Date	Features	Grade	Purchased From	Date	Price Paid	Value Now
	BR50–095	1996						
	BR50–100	1996	PROOF					
	BR50–105	1997						
	BR50–110	1997	PROOF					

25 Pounds

✓	No.	Date	Features	Grade	Purchased From	Date	Price Paid	Value Now
	BR25–005	1987						
	BR25–010	1987	PROOF					
	BR25–015	1988						
	BR25–020	1988	PROOF					
	BR25–025	1989						
	BR25–030	1989	PROOF					
	BR25–035	1990						
	BR25–040	1990	PROOF					
	BR25–045	1991						
	BR25–050	1991	PROOF					
	BR25–055	1992						
	BR25–060	1992	PROOF					
	BR25–065	1993						
	BR25–070	1993	PROOF					
	BR25–075	1994						
	BR25–080	1994	PROOF					
	BR25–085	1995						
	BR25–090	1995	PROOF					
	BR25–095	1996						
	BR25–100	1996	PROOF					
	BR25–105	1997						
	BR25–110	1997	PROOF					

10 Pounds

✓	No.	Date	Features	Grade	Purchased From	Date	Price Paid	Value Now
	BR10–005	1987						
	BR10–010	1987	PROOF					
	BR10–015	1988						
	BR10–020	1988	PROOF					
	BR10–025	1989						
	BR10–030	1989	PROOF					
	BR10–035	1990						
	BR10–040	1990	PROOF					
	BR10–045	1991						
	BR10–050	1991	PROOF					
	BR10–055	1992						
	BR10–060	1992	PROOF					
	BR10–065	1993						
	BR10–070	1993	PROOF					
	BR10–075	1994						
	BR10–080	1994	PROOF					

Cont.

✓	No.	Date	Features	*Grade*	*Purchased From*	*Date*	*Price Paid*	*Value Now*
	BR10–085	1995						
	BR10–090	1995	PROOF					
	BR10–095	1996						
	BR10–100	1996	PROOF					
	BR10–105	1997						
	BR10–110	1997	PROOF					

Proof Sets

George IV 1820 – 1830

1826

✓	No.	Date	Features	*Grade*	*Purchased From*	*Date*	*Price Paid*	*Value Now*
	PS-1826	1826	Proof					

William IV 1830 – 1837

1831

✓	No.	Date	Features	*Grade*	*Purchased From*	*Date*	*Price Paid*	*Value Now*
	PS-1831	1831	Proof					

Victoria 1837 – 1901

1839

✓	No.	Date	Features	*Grade*	*Purchased From*	*Date*	*Price Paid*	*Value Now*
	PS-1839	1839	Proof					

1853

✓	No.	Date	Features	*Grade*	*Purchased From*	*Date*	*Price Paid*	*Value Now*
	PS-1853	1853	Proof					
	PS-1877	1877	Proof					

1887

✓	No.	Date	Features	*Grade*	*Purchased From*	*Date*	*Price Paid*	*Value Now*
	PS-1887L	1887	Proof					
	PS-1887S	1887	Proof					

1893

✓	No.	Date	Features	*Grade*	*Purchased From*	*Date*	*Price Paid*	*Value Now*
	PS-1893L	1893	Proof					
	PS-1893S	1893	Proof					

Edward VII 1901 – 1910

1902

✓	No.	Date	Features	*Grade*	*Purchased From*	*Date*	*Price Paid*	*Value Now*
	PS-02L	1902	Matt Proof					
	PS-02S	1902	Matt Proof					

George V 1910 – 1936

1911

✓	No.	Date	Features	Grade	Purchased From	Date	Price Paid	Value Now
	PS-11L	1911	Proof					
	PS-11SH	1911	Proof					
	PS-11SV	1911	Proof					

1927

✓	No.	Date	Features	Grade	Purchased From	Date	Price Paid	Value Now
	PS-27	1927	Proof or Prooflike					
	PS-27SB	1927	as above; struck from sandblasted dies					

George VI 1937 – 1952

1937

✓	No.	Date	Features	Grade	Purchased From	Date	Price Paid	Value Now
	PS-37G	1937	Proof					
	PS-37S	1937	Proof					
	PS-37SSB	1937	Proof struck from sandblasted dies					
	PS-37B	1937	Proof					

1950

✓	No.	Date	Features	Grade	Purchased From	Date	Price Paid	Value Now
	PS-50	1950	Proof					
	PS-50SB	1950	Proof struck from sandblasted dies					

1951

✓	No.	Date	Features	Grade	Purchased From	Date	Price Paid	Value Now
	PS-51	1951	Proof					
	PS-51SB	1951	Proof struck from sandblasted dies					

Elizabeth II 1952 –

1953

✓	No.	Date	Features	Grade	Purchased From	Date	Price Paid	Value Now
	PS-53	1953	Proof					
	PS-53SB	1953	Proof struck from sandblasted dies					

1970

✓	No.	Date	Features	Grade	Purchased From	Date	Price Paid	Value Now
	PS-70	1970	Proof					

1971

✓	No.	Date	Features	*Grade*	*Purchased From*	*Date*	*Price Paid*	*Value Now*
	DPS-71	1971	Proof					

1972

✓	No.	Date	Features	*Grade*	*Purchased From*	*Date*	*Price Paid*	*Value Now*
	DPS-72	1972	Proof					

1973

✓	No.	Date	Features	*Grade*	*Purchased From*	*Date*	*Price Paid*	*Value Now*
	DPS-73	1973	Proof					

1974

✓	No.	Date	Features	*Grade*	*Purchased From*	*Date*	*Price Paid*	*Value Now*
	DPS-74	1974	Proof					

1975

✓	No.	Date	Features	*Grade*	*Purchased From*	*Date*	*Price Paid*	*Value Now*
	DPS-75	1975	Proof					

1976

✓	No.	Date	Features	*Grade*	*Purchased From*	*Date*	*Price Paid*	*Value Now*
	DPS-76	1976	Proof					

1977

✓	No.	Date	Features	*Grade*	*Purchased From*	*Date*	*Price Paid*	*Value Now*
	DPS-77	1977	Proof					

1978

✓	No.	Date	Features	*Grade*	*Purchased From*	*Date*	*Price Paid*	*Value Now*
	DPS-78	1978	Proof					

1979

✓	No.	Date	Features	*Grade*	*Purchased From*	*Date*	*Price Paid*	*Value Now*
	DPS-79	1979	Proof					

1980

✓	No.	Date	Features	*Grade*	*Purchased From*	*Date*	*Price Paid*	*Value Now*
	DPS-80GL	1980	Proof					
	DPS-80	1980	Proof					

1981

✓	No.	Date	Features	Grade	Purchased From	Date	Price Paid	Value Now
	DPS-81G	1981	Proof					
	DPS-81	1981	Proof					

1982

✓	No.	Date	Features	Grade	Purchased From	Date	Price Paid	Value Now
	DPS-82G	1982	Proof					
	DPS-82	1982	Proof					

1983

✓	No.	Date	Features	Grade	Purchased From	Date	Price Paid	Value Now
	DPS-83G	1983	Proof					
	DPS-83	1983	Proof					

1984

✓	No.	Date	Features	Grade	Purchased From	Date	Price Paid	Value Now
	DPS-84G	1984	Proof					
	DPS-84	1984	Proof					

1985

✓	No.	Date	Features	Grade	Purchased From	Date	Price Paid	Value Now
	DPS-85G	1985	Proof					
	DPS-85DL	1985	Proof					
	DPS-85	1985	Proof					

1986

✓	No.	Date	Features	Grade	Purchased From	Date	Price Paid	Value Now
	DPS-86G	1986	Proof					
	DPS-86DL	1986	Proof					
	DPS-86	1986	Proof					

1987

✓	No.	Date	Features	Grade	Purchased From	Date	Price Paid	Value Now
	DPS-87BRL	1987	Proof					
	DPS-87BRS	1987	Proof					
	DPS-87G	1987	Proof					
	DPS-87DL	1987	Proof					
	DPS-87	1987	Proof					

1984–1987

✓	No.	Date	Features	Grade	Purchased From	Date	Price Paid	Value Now
	DPS-84PFP	1984–87	Piedfort Proof					
	DPS-84PP	1984–87	Proof					

1988

✓	No.	Date	Features	*Grade*	*Purchased From*	*Date*	*Price Paid*	*Value Now*
	DPS-88BRL	1988	Proof					
	DPS-88BRS	1988	Proof					
	DPS-88G	1988	Proof					
	DPS-88DL	1988	Proof					
	DPS-88	1988	Proof					

1989

✓	No.	Date	Features	*Grade*	*Purchased From*	*Date*	*Price Paid*	*Value Now*
	DPS-89BRL	1989	Proof					
	DPS-89BRS	1989	Proof					
	DPS-89GL	1989	Proof					
	DPS-89GS	1989	Proof					
	DPS-89DL	1989	Proof					
	DPS-89	1989	Proof					
	DPS-89PF2P	1989	Piedfort Proof					
	DPS-89P2P	1989	Proof					

1983–1989

✓	No.	Date	Features	*Grade*	*Purchased From*	*Date*	*Price Paid*	*Value Now*
	DPS-83PFP	1983–89	Piedfort Proof					

1990

✓	No.	Date	Features	*Grade*	*Purchased From*	*Date*	*Price Paid*	*Value Now*
	DPS-90BR	1990	Proof					
	DPS-90GL	1990	Proof					
	DPS-90GS	1990	Proof					
	DPS-90DL	1990	Proof					
	DPS-90	1990	Proof					
	DPS-90–05	1990	Proof					

1991

✓	No.	Date	Features	*Grade*	*Purchased From*	*Date*	*Price Paid*	*Value Now*
	DPS-91BR	1991	Proof					
	DPS-91GL	1991	Proof					
	DPS-91GS	1991	Proof					
	DPS-91DL	1991	Proof					
	DPS-91	1991	Proof					

1992

✓	No.	Date	Features	*Grade*	*Purchased From*	*Date*	*Price Paid*	*Value Now*
	DPS-92BR	1992	Proof					
	DPS-92GL	1992	Proof					
	DPS-92GS	1992	Proof					
	DPS-92DL	1992	Proof					
	DPS-92	1992	Proof					

Cont.

✓	No.	Date	Features	Grade	Purchased From	Date	Price Paid	Value Now
	DPS-92–10	1992	Proof					

1992 1993

✓	No.	Date	Features	Grade	Purchased From	Date	Price Paid	Value Now
	DPS-92–50	1992–93 double dated coin	Proof & Piedfort Proof					

1993

✓	No.	Date	Features	Grade	Purchased From	Date	Price Paid	Value Now
	DPS-93BR	1993	Proof					
	DPS-93GL	1993	Proof					
	DPS-93GS	1993	Proof					
	DPS-93DL	1993	Proof					
	DPS-93	1993	Proof					

1994

✓	No.	Date	Features	Grade	Purchased From	Date	Price Paid	Value Now
	DPS-94BR	1994	Proof					
	DPS-94GL	1994	Proof					
	DPS-94GS	1994	Proof					
	DPS-94DL	1994	Proof					
	DPS-94	1994	Proof					

1995

✓	No.	Date	Features	Grade	Purchased From	Date	Price Paid	Value Now
	DPS-95BR	1995	Proof					
	DPS-95GL	1995	Proof					
	DPS-95GS	1995	Proof					
	DPS-95DL	1995	Proof					
	DPS-95	1995	Proof					

1996

✓	No.	Date	Features	Grade	Purchased From	Date	Price Paid	Value Now
	DPS-96DL	1996	Proof					
	DPS-96	1996	Proof					

1997

✓	No.	Date	Features	Grade	Purchased From	Date	Price Paid	Value Now
	DPS-97BR	1997	Proof					
	DPS-97GL	1997	Proof					
	DPS-97GS	1997	Proof					
	DPS-97DL	1997	Proof					
	DPS-97	1997	Proof					

Specimen and Mint Sets

Elizabeth II 1952 –

1953

✓	No.	Date	Features	*Grade*	*Purchased From*	*Date*	*Price Paid*	*Value Now*
	MS-53	1953	Currency					

1968/1971

✓	No.	Date	Features	*Grade*	*Purchased From*	*Date*	*Price Paid*	*Value Now*
	DMS-68	1968/1971	Currency					

1982

✓	No.	Date	Features	*Grade*	*Purchased From*	*Date*	*Price Paid*	*Value Now*
	DMS-82	1982	Specimen					

1983

✓	No.	Date	Features	*Grade*	*Purchased From*	*Date*	*Price Paid*	*Value Now*
	DMS-83	1983	Specimen					
	DMS-83E	1983	Specimen					

1984

✓	No.	Date	Features	*Grade*	*Purchased From*	*Date*	*Price Paid*	*Value Now*
	DMS-84	1984	Specimen					

1985

✓	No.	Date	Features	*Grade*	*Purchased From*	*Date*	*Price Paid*	*Value Now*
	DMS-85	1985	Specimen					

1986

✓	No.	Date	Features	*Grade*	*Purchased From*	*Date*	*Price Paid*	*Value Now*
	DMS-86	1986	Specimen					

1987

✓	No.	Date	Features	*Grade*	*Purchased From*	*Date*	*Price Paid*	*Value Now*
	DMS-87	1987	Specimen					

1988

✓	No.	Date	Features	*Grade*	*Purchased From*	*Date*	*Price Paid*	*Value Now*
	DMS-88	1988	Specimen					

1989

✓	No.	Date	Features	Grade	Purchased From	Date	Price Paid	Value Now
	DMS-89	1989	Specimen					
	DMS-89–2P	1989	Specimen					

1990

✓	No.	Date	Features	Grade	Purchased From	Date	Price Paid	Value Now
	DMS-90	1990	Specimen					

1991

✓	No.	Date	Features	Grade	Purchased From	Date	Price Paid	Value Now
	DMS-91	1991	Specimen					

1992

✓	No.	Date	Features	Grade	Purchased From	Date	Price Paid	Value Now
	DMS-92	1992	Specimen					

1993

✓	No.	Date	Features	Grade	Purchased From	Date	Price Paid	Value Now
	DMS-93	1993	Specimen					

1994

✓	No.	Date	Features	Grade	Purchased From	Date	Price Paid	Value Now
	DMS-94	1994	Specimen					

1995

✓	No.	Date	Features	Grade	Purchased From	Date	Price Paid	Value Now
	DMS-95	1995	Specimen					

1996

✓	No.	Date	Features	Grade	Purchased From	Date	Price Paid	Value Now
	DMS-96	1996	Specimen					

1997

✓	No.	Date	Features	Grade	Purchased From	Date	Price Paid	Value Now
	DMS-97	1997	Specimen					

Notes